Just-in-Time

Just-in-Time

Surviving
by Breaking Tradition

Walter E. Goddard

THE OLIVER WIGHT COMPANIES

Oliver Wight Limited Publications, Inc.
5 Oliver Wight Drive
Essex Junction, VT 05452

Library of Congress Catalog
Card Number: 8661728

ISBN: 0-939246-07-4

Printed in the United States of America by
Maple-Vail Book Manufacturing Group

7 8 9 10

Contents

Preface   *vii*

Acknowledgments   *ix*

1   Doing the Basics Better   *1*

2   Setting the Course   9

3   Building a Just-in-Time Environment   25

4   The Thinking Worker—The Secret Weapon   47

5   Shrinking Order Quantities   63

6   Taking the Quality High Road   75

7   Producing Valid Schedules   93

8   Demand Pull   *111*

9   Product, Plant, and Process   *117*

10 Excellent Vendor Performance   *127*

11 The Marketing Edge   *149*

12 Software   *159*

13 Measurements—Accounting for Just-in-Time   *165*

14 The Continually Improving Process   *175*

Appendix A: Sources for Additional Information   *181*

Glossary   *183*

Bibliography   *193*

Index   *197*

Preface

This book is about what people in manufacturing companies are doing to survive in an increasingly competitive world. It's real world—the experiences of people and companies—not theory or conjecture. Although all persons featured in this book would downplay their contribution, each has helped their company make tremendous improvements and is willing to share how.

The manufacturing companies have little in common. They are different in size, process, and products. However, all are successful businesses largely due to capable managers who are not satisfied with business as usual. Each company has an urgent requirement to reduce costs, inventories, and lead times, as well as a pressing need to improve deliveries, quality, and productivity.

Just-in-Time is the organized process to make this happen. It is not a sudden awakening that these things are important, as they have always been. Rather, it's a realization and new dedication that they are everyone's job. It's not a dramatic solution for achieving these improvements. Rather, it's an innovative, practical approach capable of generating dramatic results.

Success travels quickly. Most executives attending our top management classes are familiar with the term Just-in-Time. Yet few are actively implementing it.

If it's so good, why isn't everyone doing it? The reasons are many: Executives are saturated with buzz words and acronyms; consequently, many are turned off by what they perceive as one more quick fix. Some see Just-in-Time as more fluff than substance—too vague to turn into an action plan. Some say, "It applies to high-volume repetitive environments, but we're different." Finally, many companies just don't have the time to pursue another "opportunity," regardless of the eventual value.

Each of these reactions is understandable. Certainly, we don't need another acronym; there are plenty of those already. Although companies are reporting early benefits during implementation, Just-in-Time definitely takes time. The Just-in-Time trail is still being blazed, but valid hindsight is available. There are always more high-priority projects in a company than there is available talent, and Just-in-Time requires far more than simply management encouragement. Nevertheless, once understood, no one can refute the universal logic of Just-in-Time nor the documented benefits.

Our goal is to increase your understanding of Just-in-Time so you can apply it to your job and your company. We have structured the book by broad categories and have laced each with the experiences of practitioners. These people, and a great many others, will continue to expand the body of knowledge beyond the boundaries of this book. However, we have learned enough to be confident of our advice and to know we need to keep working with the leading edge companies to learn more.

Walter E. Goddard
Sunapee, New Hampshire

Acknowledgments

The best research and development department in industry has always been the trenches of progressive companies. In these fertile grounds new ideas are tested, and only what works survives and expands. The Oliver Wight Companies selected seven such manufacturing companies, knowing that each had excellent control systems and were aggressively persuing Just-in-Time.

As a group we met in September 1985 to compare experiences, identify prerequisites, and to map out implementation steps. Let me introduce the team:

Bently Nevada: Ray Bacon, Vice President of Manufacturing

Black and Decker: Ken Good, Production and Inventory Control Manager, Consumer Power Tools Division; and Ed Parrish, CIM Manager

Hewlett-Packard: Charlene Adair, Specialist Manufacturing and Quality Systems; and Vivian Wright, Manufacturing Specialist

Steelcase: Gary Vredenburg, Plant Manager, File Plant; and Rob Burch, Manager, Production Planning and Inventory Control, Systems II

Tennant Company: Duane Davis, Superintendent

Tektronix: Mike Caravatta, MRP/JIT Training Internal Consultant; and Ralph Todd, Business Operations Consultant

Xerox: Pierre Landry, Materials Management

The four people from the Oliver Wight Companies were Roger Brooks, Dave Garwood, Walt Goddard, and Tom Wallace. The insights of Roger, Dave, and Tom added significantly to the conference. Just as important was all of the work each put in afterward to ensure that the book measured up to its potential. Anyone can make a subject complicated, but the three of them made certain the explanation of Just-in-Time retained the essence of simplicity.

Following the conference a number of Oliver Wight people visited the above-mentioned companies to gather more data and worked with other good Just-in-Time users: Don Rice, Manufacturing Administrator of APCOM; Don MacKellar, UK Supply Director at Cummins Engine; Pat Keane, Project Manager at Harley-Davidson; Vern Pearson, Production Manager at Omark Industries; and Bruce Harvey, Senior Manufacturing Consultant at Hewlett-Packard. All were generous in explaining what they were doing and anxious to hear what others had accomplished.

Special mention must be made of the exceptional contributions of Darryl Landvater, President of Oliver Wight Video Productions, Inc. Three other Oliver Wight associates—Dick Ling, Andre Martin, and Al Stevens—were excellent critiquers of the many drafts. Thanks also go to Charlene Adair, who provided many hours of help following the conference. We salute Ron Schultz and Dana Scannell for digesting tons of material and converting it into a readable text. Ron is a professional writer, and Dana is General Manager of Oliver Wight Limited Publications, Inc.

It was a team effort, start to finish. Only a few people could represent the participating companies, yet all employees contributed. More than a few of my associates added, subtracted, and clarified words, yet only my name appears as the author. It's an honor to represent this dedicated group.

Just-in-Time

Chapter 1

Doing the Basics Better

"IN BUSINESS THERE'S NO PAR, JUST COMPETITION"

JUST-IN-TIME ON LINE

The first thing we notice about the receiving dock at Hewlett-Packard's Vancouver, Washington, facility is how small it is. Three outside delivery bays open to a room the size of some living rooms. There are no racks filled to overflowing awaiting disposition. There are no stacks of aged inventory gathering dust. There are also no expediters darting in and out. Why? Because this is the beginning of a Just-in-Time manufacturing process at work, and working.

We see a handful of cartons on a flexible metal roller track. It is a track that stretches out to the delivery trucks making their daily deliveries of parts to the plant. The track then runs past a stockroom computer terminal where a bar-coded label is attached as packages are received. The label tells the handler whether the received goods can go directly into plant distribution or whether they need to go to incoming inspection. The transaction also tells accounting and procurement that the shipment has arrived.

The track then splits into a top and bottom level and travels through receiving and incoming inspection. The reason for the two tracks is that Hewlett-Packard (H-P) does not inspect every delivery that is made. Only material from vendors who are new to H-P's process, or have had quality problems in the past, must stop at incoming inspection. Except for an occasional quality audit, the rest travel on the top track directly over incoming inspection to a distribution and dispersement point. From here, the parts are delivered out into the production environment.

This process from dock to work-in-process (WIP) takes two and

1

one-half hours on the average. It used to take two or three days, and the material terminated in the stockroom, not on the production floor.

The Hewlett-Packard shop floor is a broad, well-lit, columned facility. The plant is extremely clean and very well kept. H-P has a favorite housecleaning saying that can be found on signs spread around the plant. It says simply, "Clean-up After Yourself, Your Mother Doesn't Work Here." It's an effective campaign.

At this particular facility in Washington, Hewlett-Packard builds their impact, thermal, and ink jet line printers. They're running two daily eight-hour shifts and producing about 116 units a day, across four assembly lines.

The assembly process itself begins with the frame that has been shipped to H-P already in the shipping container. The frame vendor purchases the shipping carton, packages the frame inside, and ships it to H-P. The entire product is built on this shipping container, which facilitates handling as it rolls along the track through assembly and eventually into shipping. The best part of this is that the workers and management together came up with this idea! It has saved material, tools, and several handling steps.

Major improvements on the printed circuit (PC) board line have had a huge impact on work-in-process. It is on this line that H-P has dramatically reduced equipment setup times. At one point, H-P made each PC board in batches on their auto-insertion machines. It would then take them hours to set up the machines again to run the next size lot. But after listening to their operator's suggestions, engineering then implemented the changes to meet the operator's and product's needs. This included retooling the machine, which applied the various components on the printed circuit board. By doing this, they have virtually eliminated their setup time, allowing H-P to produce in one-for-one order quantities. The effect that this reduction in order quantity has had on quality and inventory throughout the plant is extraordinary.

Once the subassemblies have arrived just in time, and the printers are assembled, they are run through a comprehensive testing. They are then rolled down the final length of track to shipping. At this time they are assigned to their specific sales order and given a new bar-code label; the shipping orders are then attached, and the printer rides to the end of the line as finished goods. But there are no material handlers taking these finished products into inventory. They are simply shipped directly to their customers. H-P turns over their finished goods inventory daily.

From dock to shipping, the process takes a day. It used to take them seven days to build the same product. The same output also took over twice the amount of space and 30 percent more people.

The goal at the plant is to produce the daily schedule. Once that day's schedule is met, the operators stop work. If there is still time on their shift they may go into quality circles to discuss any problems they may be having. Or they may see to some preventive maintenance on their tools, cycle count their parts, attend a training session, or continue their housekeeping. And on those occasions when everything is done early, they go home, even if there is still time before the end of their shift. They are still paid for a full eight hours.

If the production schedule is being met, Hewlett-Packard believes they gain nothing by building inventory. Instead they build better employee relations. The system is working. But then it had better work, because if it doesn't, Hewlett-Packard might not be in the printer business at all.

Though Hewlett-Packard's Vancouver plant is an example of a repetitive manufacturer, building the same products over and over with fairly high volume and low mix, Just-in-Time can benefit any environment, even one where each product built is unique. It is the link that a Just-in-Time approach makes between a manufacturer, their supplier and their customers that makes this happen.

But there are other factors at work, which may not be as obvious as the flow that visibly occurs in a plant. We see material moving through the plant as needed, but what is invisible is the flow of information that makes certain the right parts arrive at the right spot at the right time. What is also not seen is the hard work that went into producing the success of the various operations. These invisible steps make what is seen in the plant significant. The physical process may begin on the receiving dock, but the overall Just-in-Time approach began much earlier. It started with people challenging the way business has always been done.

Our intent, then, is to expose both the visible aspects of Just-in-Time, and those *not* seen. We hope to illuminate the process in a manner that will allow a company to decide how to make it work best for them. In so doing, it will become evident that Just-in-Time is the effective marriage between the people, the plant, and the systems operating in a manufacturing environment. Working in harmony, these three elements make the process flow.

THERE IS NO MORE BUSINESS AS USUAL

The Queen said to Alice, "It takes all the running you can to stay in the same place." To keep ahead of the game in today's highly competitive global economy, a company has to not only run a little faster, it has to run farther too. American manufacturing finds itself at a precarious point in the world competitive standing, a point where even when it's running as fast as it thinks it can, it still may be losing ground. Foreign competition has proved to be far more formidable than American manufacturing would like to think. This means that new approaches have to be found and applied in order to survive. If the threat is ignored, there is no question it will continue to have a major negative influence on our economy and standard of living.

Oliver Wight said, "In business there's no par, just competition." This certainly holds true in today's marketplace. Global competition is not only playing our game, it is beating us in too many industries. Xerox Corporation's Pierre Landry put his finger directly on the pulse of the problem when he said, "The Japanese have already eaten our lunch, now they're eating our dessert." In other words, if something is not done we may well lose our share of the marketplace pie. Luckily for companies like Xerox and Hewlett-Packard, they saw their places at the table being snatched away before it was too late, and they have aggressively gone out to meet the challenge. But to do so, they have had to make some major changes in the way they do business.

The American people make up only 5 percent of the global population. If American manufacturing is going to stand a chance in the world marketplaces, changes are going to have to be made. In hopes of initiating those changes, teams of American businessmen have made pilgrimages to successful Japanese manufacturing companies to see what they are doing so differently. Many are struck by the cultural aspects, the collective society that seems to be willing to acquiesce to the greater good of the company. But that is not the main reason the Japanese have been so successful in manufacturing.

The key is simple. The Japanese are constantly examining their process and asking, "Why does it have to be that way? Just because that's the way it has always been doesn't mean it can't be changed and made better." They're challenging everything. They have accepted the creed that it is no longer business as usual! It was at this point that Just-in-Time became a reality.

What has been seen by visitors to the East isn't just a marginal rise in the standards of performance, it's a dramatic increase. While American businessmen were out trying to break the barrier of the four minute mile, hailing their success when they reached 3.9, the Japanese businessmen figured out how to eliminate their wasted moves to run a one minute mile. It changed the whole game. The Harbor Study demonstrated how the Japanese were able to produce basically the same car as the Americans for $1718 less and in half the time. (See Figure 1-1.)

This industrial barrier busting is by no means something that is unique to the Japanese. Henry Ford brought about the same sort of process-shattering change after the turn of the century.

Superior Technology	$73
Better Management Systems	
Quality Control	329
Just-in-Time Production Techniques	550
Materials Handling Engineering	41
Other (Quality Circles, Job Classification)	478
Total, Better Management Systems	1,398
Union-Management Relations	
Less Absenteeism	81
More Flexible Relief Systems and Allowances	89
Union Representation	12
Total, Union-Management Relations	182
Lower Wages and Fringe Benefits	550
Total Cost Advantage to Japanese	2,203
Less: Shipping Costs	485
Net Cost Advantage to Japanese	$1,718

(*New York Times,* 2/16/83, "Why GM Needs Toyota")

SMALL CAR

US	59.9 hours	4250 people
Japan	30.8 hours	2360 people

Figure 1-1. Harbor Study

WE'D BE MORE COMPETITIVE IF . . .

The American answer today to the success of manufacturing offshore tends to point to the cost of labor. But even Henry Ford knew, "You do not increase your profits by taking it from your suppliers or from your workers. What you do is put more brains into the process." This is exactly what the competition has done with Just-in-Time. They have paid attention to detail and attacked the manufacturing process head on, questioning all production steps right down to the design of the product. Just-in-Time isn't a new idea. There is precedence right here in America for addressing these same issues. Just-in-Time offers an approach and a set of tools to make the job work. Just-in-Time is getting back to basics, and doing them better.

To stop the hemorrhage resulting from jobs going offshore, American manufacturing has to start supplying its people with the facility to compete. The people can make it happen, but they need management support and understanding to assure success. Surveys have shown that less than 30 percent of manufacturing companies have effective techniques in place to deal with this problem, and two thirds of those companies feel there is significant room for improvement in how they use the techniques. With labor costing only 10 cents on the manufacturing dollar, it is not the cost per labor hour that counts, it is the total cost *per unit*. Manufacturing must start looking at the real problems plaguing their plants: wasteful practices.

The Just-in-Time answer is to focus action: to make every action, every investment, every second, and every person count. Eliminate anything and everything that doesn't contribute, and when we're done, do it again—better, and then once more—even better.

THE COMPETITIVE EDGE

How does this make a company more competitive? A company is judged on the appearance, soundness, and innovation of its product, in addition to its performance, cost, service and quality. If all companies produced a functional product with similar characteristics, it would reduce competition to the final three elements of cost, service, and quality. By attacking the wasteful items in the process, and providing and meeting valid schedules, manufacturing can significantly lower costs, improve quality, and quickly service the needs of its customers. That's being competitive, and it is being done regularly within this country, today.

It is important to note that we are not going to present a theoretical treatise on solving the ills of American manufacturing. Rather, you will find in the pages to come an applied, proven, and practical look into American companies which, like the Japanese, are no longer content with merely running fast. They're running faster, and then faster still.

These companies have embarked on a journey toward manufacturing excellence. The ship on which they sail is the company-wide approach called Just-in-Time. This is not just another bandwagon slogan. It is a long-term commitment to being the best. At one time or another in their evolution, the companies quoted in the pages to come have all been over their heads in the confusion and wastefulness of the manufacturing process. But they realized the importance of getting a leg up on the competition, and they realized the only way to do it was to question every aspect of their process and then work harder and smarter to fix it.

Interestingly, most of the companies that participated in this book said they did not get into Just-in-Time because they wanted to. They got into Just-in-Time because they *had to*. It was what they needed to do if they wanted to be around in five, ten, or fifteen years. They knew the time to act was upon them, and they began, dedicating and committing every man, woman, and machine to achieving the ultimate goal of manufacturing excellence.

This is not a pipe dream based on words without deeds. These companies went to the source. They demanded quality. They activated their employees, attacking waste everywhere. They reduced setups, shrinking excessive inventory. They produced and executed valid schedules. They reduced work-in-process and cycle time. They brought their vendors on board while reducing their vendor base. They built trust at every level and involved every person in the process from the CEO to the person sweeping the floors. Nothing was sacred, and everybody profited.

If those ideals seem like the impossible dream, if it seems like the costs to implement such a program would go beyond the scope of most companies, if it seems like something that could never happen in your company, read on and find out how it is done. It makes so much sense, you'll be kicking yourself for not doing it before.

It takes courage, dedication, desire, and a lot of hard work to be the best. It takes those things just to be good. But to excel means to be constantly raising the high bar. If you're trying to high-jump seven feet and the competition has already cleared the bar at twenty, it is going to take some pretty hard and fast work to stay in the game.

The companies supporting the ideas presented in this book demonstrate how they began meeting this challenge in a variety of manufacturing environments. They are on the journey toward manufacturing excellence. Through what they know today, these companies have shown that it is possible to achieve their ideals, but only if they constantly replace their old ideals with new ones. Just-in-Time says you may be good, but you can be better. For most, the trip is not a painless one, but the discomfort far outweighs the alternatives—being eaten out of house and home by competition.

This, then, is a book about the actualization of America's competitive future. It is a report on the state of Just-in-Time in 1986. We will learn more in the years to come as it continues to evolve. For now, this will help serve as a practical outline of how to breathe new life into weary companies. This book is about preserving jobs, while producing high-performance, high-quality products at the lowest cost and shipping them on time.

Just-in-Time is an attitude, not an algorithm. It's a never-ending challenge, not a fixed target. It's the old American spirit: back to basics. But most importantly, it's proven. It works. The experience and validation of those companies we have spoken with is the best yardstick we can provide to measure and compare what *can* be accomplished with what *has been* accomplished. It is the synthesis of their actions that makes the process work. It's their participation that makes the message of this book truly important.

Chapter 2

Setting the Course

What does Just-in-Time mean to a company? By way of analogy we offer this story as an answer to that question. Two hunters are out hunting in the mountains when they suddenly catch sight of a huge grizzly bear coming right for them. They immediately turn tail and start running as fast as they can. Looking over their shoulders, all they can see is that grizzly licking his lips and gaining on them fast. All of a sudden one of the hunters sits down on the ground, takes off his backpack, and then starts taking off his hiking boots. Diving into his backpack, he pulls out a pair of running shoes. His partner looks back at him, and in utter surprise yells, "You're crazy! That bear's going to get us, and you're changing your shoes?" The first hunter calmly looks up as he finishes lacing his shoes and says, "I don't have to worry about outrunning that bear, I just have to outrun you!"

Just-in-Time offers a company the opportunity to gain that extra step on the competition. There are no secret formulas to the approach. Just-in-Time is based primarily on the ideas of simplicity and common sense. To that extent, many of the elements of a Just-in-Time approach are already in place in manufacturing companies around the country. Just-in-Time is not a technique, but rather an integrating and focusing mechanism to better apply many of those existing elements.

We have defined Just-in-Time as:

An approach to achieving excellence in a manufacturing company based on the continuing elimination of waste and consistent improvement in productivity. Waste is then defined as those activities that do not add value to the product.

Traditionally, manufacturing in America has lived by the creed "More is Better." In regards to suppliers, the more vendors in competition for a company's business, the better. The larger the quantities ordered from those vendors, the better the price. Since some suppliers can never be trusted to deliver on time, or to give the customer the kind of quality necessary, it's become necessary to carry a large safety stock. Then once everything is delivered, it must be inspected to make certain the quality is at least acceptable. Business as usual.

The stockroom reveals the result. Inventory is frequently piled high in the aisles, and material handlers and expediters search relentlessly for needed parts. Reordering of materials is based on a "just in case" approach. Out on the shop floor, workers carry on their activities the best they can with the materials they have. Larger-than-needed batches of components are built to amortize the costs of lengthy machine setup times. These items are then sent to stores, or pushed on to the next stage, where queues of work-in-process pile up ahead of machine centers. Ask some operators about those queues, and they will smile and say, "Job security. If we can see it, we know we're not out of work." Business as usual.

Upper management has annual planning meetings, where the chief executive officer and others outline the direction for the coming year: Lower costs and increase productivity. Marketing presents forecasts of increased sales, and engineering presents plans for highly sophisticated new products. Business as usual.

On the shop floor, supervisors tell their operators about these plans and what will be expected of them. They proudly point to their newest press, which they plan to run a million strokes at a time. Lead times are planned in weeks and months because that's just how long it takes. Quality inspectors assure the quality of the product is acceptable. On-time delivery to the customer on special orders has consistently been 70 percent on time. For make-to-stock products, shipping off the shelf is 95 percent on time, but this requires a very large finished goods inventory from which to draw. Business as usual.

Unfortunately, business as usual isn't cutting it anymore. One of the aims of Just-in-Time is to meet a schedule every day that satisfies the product demand. Anything more or less is waste. Quality is measured not in percentage points but as defects in parts per million. Inventory doesn't stand or sit; it flows. Single-digit inventory turnovers are being replaced by thirty to fifty inventory turns a year, and more in some cases. What this allows is raw material, which has arrived in the morning, being shipped that afternoon in finished products.

The Japanese made the world manufacturing community take notice when they began producing these results, and balancing their production and demand rates. They did it by changing the way they think: by attacking large economic order quantities, by no longer accepting long setups as a constant, by attacking quality issues (scrap is nothing but waste), by reducing their vendor bases and making partners of their suppliers, by shrinking inventory in the stockroom and on the factory floor, and by involving and respecting every employee in the entire operation. They attacked every aspect of the manufacturing process, slaying the sacred cows. In so doing, they produced Just-in-Time.

LAYING THE FOUNDATION

Exactly where in Japan the approach of Just-in-Time was born is still up for speculation. Some say it began over twenty-five years ago in the Japanese shipyards, when inventories were lowered because of the ready access of steelworks. Few, though, would quarrel with the fact that the real father of Just-in-Time was Toyota Motor Corporation's Taiichi Ohno. It was Ohno's organization of his own ideas together with those brought forward by his subordinates and Toyota's workers that produced what is called the Toyota Production System, of which Just-in-Time is the overriding process.

Toyota's definition of a Just-in-Time system is to produce "only necessary items in a necessary quantity at a necessary time." This Toyota Production System is often mistakenly referred to as the "Kanban System." Kanban is the Japanese word for "sign, or visible record." Though the Toyota Production System does in fact use kanban cards as the material movement aspect of their approach, Just-in-Time, the Toyota Production System, and the kanban card are not one in the same. Just-in-Time is a company-wide approach, a set of objectives, and not merely a set of techniques. We will discuss this distinction in greater detail in Chapter 7.

The Just-in-Time approach gained widespread support in Japan during the oil crunch of 1973. Japan, having little natural resources of its own, and highly dependent on foreign energy sources, had to find a way to conserve in order to survive. It was during this worldwide crisis, while other Japanese companies were treading water as fast as possible just to stay afloat, that Toyota's continued profits began to attract attention.

Toyota satisfied their objectives for reducing costs by examining the effect their operations had on three distinct groupings: people, plant and systems.

1. *People*.   Without the involvement and commitment of people, from top to bottom, in every manufacturing operation and process, Just-in-Time would be nothing more than a theoretical exercise. It's people who must implement and carry out the objectives of Just-in-Time.

2. *Plant*.   This area includes the physical process itself, in regards to both lay-out and production. If quality is poor, or the plant is out of control, Just-in-Time might as well be Somewhere-Else-in-Time.

3. *Systems*.   Without valid schedules to plan, order, and execute, Just-in-Time will deliver some benefits (as in the area of setup time reduction) but not nearly what it could. To accomplish this, it takes computer systems to help with the massive data manipulation needed to support the activities of the company.

It is only through the active combination and interaction of these three elements that Just-in-Time can deliver significant results.

The umbrella of Just-in-Time is vast, covering a wide array of manufacturing objectives and some well-honed techniques. Together these factors are providing spectacular results. Again, each of the elements of Just-in-Time has as its ultimate focus the elimination of waste.

One of the primary areas of waste in a manufacturing environment comes from poor quality. Just-in-Time has as one of its objectives the notion of Zero Defects. This involves an approach known as Total Quality Control, which calls on techniques like Statistical Process Control, preventive maintenance, good housekeeping, manufacturable designs, and constructive vendor relations and programs.

Large inventories are another source of waste. To reduce this excess in a Just-in-Time process, order quantities and setup times need to be reduced, while at the same time the company is seeing to the problem of mismatched parts caused by poor scheduling. Then as inventory reductions occur, a company should be prepared for quality and process problems to surface. It is essential that these problems be solved at the same rate as the reduction takes place. We will examine these issues in greater detail in Chapter 9.

We will also discuss some of the other techniques companies have used to lower inventories, such as cellular manufacturing, point-of-use inventory, flexible manufacturing and line balancing. These in turn result in minimizing the levels of the bills of material and generally simplifying operations. These issues will also be explained in Chapter 9.

In order to decrease product build time, it is important to reduce work-in-process inventory. To do so, companies have employed techniques such as mixed model scheduling and reduced setups while lowering order quantities and instituting total quality control. Combined together with valid scheduling and the direct involvement of operators, all levels of management, and engineering, these ingredients will ultimately result in 100 percent schedule attainment and faster response to the marketplace.

This book will examine each of these objectives and techniques from a variety of perspectives. Since the Just-in-Time approach is a total company process for manufacturing, it is not linear, but circular. There is no one particular place to enter the loop and begin the Just-in-Time process. Each company will have its own needs, its own specific focus to pursue. This circular nature means that a company must take a close look at all their operations to best decide where to place their emphasis. Omark Industries began by reducing order quantities. Xerox, after beginning in-house, focused on dealing with their vendors. Black and Decker began with improving material flow. Tektronix began by improving their scheduling system. Each of these companies directed their efforts on the place that was causing them the most problems, where they had the greatest expertise, or where they felt they would get the greatest payback. In Chapter 3 we'll offer some guidelines as to how to pick the right area for a particular company to begin. Nonetheless, no matter where a company begins the process, there are still some specific ingredients necessary for success.

One issue a company must realize is that Just-in-Time is not a quick fix. Any organization that has tried to eliminate the need to make or buy more than is really needed has run headlong into the problem of poor quality. Striving for zero defects is a difficult and time-consuming undertaking.

Similar problems arise when attempting to deal with setup times. Reducing setup times requires engineering time, operator time, and time to retool and standardize equipment, and then practice in order to be properly implemented. These are not things that happen overnight.

Managers today want fast results, and they'd love to have a quick fix to control a situation that has been out of control for years. Managers who produce results realize that major projects such as implementing Just-in-Time demand aggressive actions. They must have the patience and staying power to effectively install a long-range project. It should be noted, though, that the majority of companies involved in this book all experienced results within the first few months of beginning their pilot programs. Even so, Just-in-Time, like most self-improvement projects, must be viewed as a journey and not a destination.

PRIMARY INGREDIENTS FOR SUCCESS

Hewlett-Packard's Charlene Adair has called Just-in-Time a "back to the basics" approach. This means to begin the process it is necessary to examine the products and the process from a fresh perspective, starting with a clean slate. In doing so, there are a number of primary ingredients that must be addressed by every company wishing to start the Just-in-Time journey.

PRIMARY INGREDIENT #1—PEOPLE INVOLVEMENT

Scrawled across the top of a noteboard in the office of Steelcase's Rob Burch are the words, "People, People, People, People, People, People." Ask any successful Just-in-Time user what the most important ingredient for their success is and you'll hear a resounding, "People!"

Unlike company-wide programs which dictated to the direct-labor workers how things were to be done, Just-in-Time says, We can't do this without *your* input. What *you* think not only matters, but it's essential! Implementing Just-in-Time properly is definitely a bottom-up process as well as top-down.

It is important to create an environment that fosters the idea that the direct-labor personnel are the experts at what they do. This may cause a bit of initial skepticism on labor's part, but there are ways for management to crack this nut. Omark Industries, in Portland, Oregon, handled this skepticism in a rather unique way. As evidence of how important they feel their people are to the process, Omark took a white piece of carpet, and put it into the plant in a heavy traffic area. They then let people walk over the carpet to find out what color it would turn. After several weeks they sent the carpet to the mill and matched the color. They then installed this dirty grey colored carpeting throughout their offices so that no worker would ever feel unwelcome walking in any manager's office.

Vern Pearson is Omark's Production Manager, and as he says, "If we're talking about priorities in terms of Just-in-Time, I guess people would be number one. I'm only as good as the people in my organization. If we don't have people involvement we don't have anything. The people out in the plant make it happen."

The people do make Just-in-Time happen—creating an environment that realizes the importance of teamwork and open communication which bring benefits that show up directly in the profit column. At many of the plants we visited, there were readily accessible flip charts on the factory floor for employee comments and suggestions. These comments were not only encouraged, they were acted upon. By making the operator the expert, new ideas to constantly refine the system arise and are then willingly implemented by them because they are directly responsible for the improvement.

This opening of the communication lines between labor and management produces a contagious excitement from the ground up. People want to be involved if they feel their involvement is valued. This excitement offers the worker at all levels a sense of intensity, an enthusiasm, a sense of mission. These are not phony, idle thoughts designed to let workers think they're important. It's realizing that they *are* important. By bringing them into the process, they feel ownership. They feel that they can make a difference.

Once leadership has been established in this area, that people are the key to a company's success, the high bar starts going up in direct proportion. Despite what those more cynical types may think, people want to do what is right. They want to produce good quality. They want to feel pride. When management really gives them the opportunity, and the tools, Just-in-Time saves dollars and makes sense.

PRIMARY INGREDIENT #2—HIGH QUALITY

Running a Just-in-Time program without good quality is begging for failure. Quality has been defined by Phil Crosby as "conformance to requirements." In other words, the product or part must meet the design specification. Since Just-in-Time is predicated on having the right part at the right time, quality is essential. Bad parts mean parts aren't available when they are needed. When a company is producing order quantities of one, not having acceptable parts available can shut down the line. But quality in a Just-in-Time environment is more than just making sure the parts are made right; it means that each person is responsible for quality. This is called "quality at the source."

As is the nature of Just-in-Time, the process of quality involves everyone. As order quantities are being reduced, the amount of inventory in stock and in work-in-process is also reduced. This shortens the time between production and usage, which in turn shortens the quality feedback loop, thus making it possible to detect problems sooner.

Quality is a matter of responsibility and paying attention to detail. There has been a long history established with an implied lower standard, that somebody down the line worried about quality. When quality at the source was removed in favor of quality inspected into the product, accountability was taken from the operator. It was someone else's job to see to quality. Now with lower quantities being produced, and less inventory traveling down the line, poor quality can be rooted out at the source. Problems can be spotted more easily; accountability is more directly linked; and people can work together to correct the causes of the poor quality.

The fallout of an excellent quality program is less scrap, less rework, and less buffer stock, all of which translates into less inventory and better on-time production rates. The aim in terms of quality is not to produce merely acceptable quality levels but continually improving quality levels, thus moving from defects measured in a 2-5 percent scrap rate to a few parts per million. The objective is 100 percent quality.

In Chapter 6 we will examine more closely the various aspects of quality programs that are achieving these numbers. As mentioned earlier these included elements such as Total Quality Control, Statistical Process Control, Quality Circles, and Preventive Maintenance.

PRIMARY INGREDIENT #3—GAINING CONTROL OF THE BUSINESS—GOOD SCHEDULES

What we have been discussing up until now are the visible aspects of manufacturing with which Just-in-Time must interact. These are obvious areas like quality, design engineering, preventive maintenance, and the like. There are also invisible areas of manufacturing that are not as obvious. But even though they are unseen, they are still absolutely necessary ingredients for Just-in-Time to work. These are the issues associated with valid schedules.

If you've ever worked for a company that had hot lists and expediters hurrying product through production, you've been forced to work with poor schedules. If end-of-the-month crunch is a ritual rather than a rare exception, you've experienced the invisible problems of poor scheduling. If past-due purchase orders are normal and past due work orders a continually recurring event, then you've worked for a company plagued by poor scheduling.

Are surprises the order of the day? Does capacity rarely equal the amount of work that needs to be done? Is overtime a regular occurrence? Do material shortages crop up at the worst possible times? Do late deliveries exceed 20 percent? Are mismatched parts a problem even though there are piles of inventory in the stockroom? Is there little or no accountability in your company for these issues? Is it always someone else's fault that things aren't right? If these issues sound familiar, then you've been suffering from poor schedules.

Fortunately, there is a cure for these ills known as valid schedules. It's fairly easy to determine if a company has valid schedules or not. Two questions need to be asked: (1) Are the schedules correct? That is, do they properly reflect the needs of the company? (2) Are they attainable? If they are followed, do they produce what the company wants on time? If the answer is yes to both, then none of the problems mentioned above should be a source of pain for the company.

With valid schedules there is no end-of-the-month crunch because production has been balanced throughout the month. There are no hot lists, because parts have been ordered in matched sets and within the necessary lead time. Expediters can be assigned to other areas in the plant because customer orders are being properly scheduled. Material shortages are soon a forgotten nightmare because material planning has been effectively installed. Late supplier deliveries are now the exception thanks to vendor schedules that offer clear visibility for suppliers, and those that are late are properly communicated and rescheduled. On-time deliveries to customers are 90 percent or better because of the accumulated effect of valid schedules.

These are not impossible goals. There are companies in this country and around the world that operate routinely in this fashion. Most are using Manufacturing Resource Planning to address these issues. Some highly repetitive companies, though, are using the planning and scheduling system that is part of the Toyota Production System. We'll talk about both of these in greater detail in Chapter 7.

EXCELLENT VENDOR PERFORMANCE

One specific area directly affected by valid schedules, which bears separate mention, is vendor performance. When it comes to purchasing and dealing with vendors, trying to get them to deliver just in time can sound to them like something akin to an out-of-control nightmare. This is especially true if the integrity of a customer's schedules is bad.

If skepticism abounds, there's good reason. These people know how out of control their customer's company may have been. Their constantly changing schedules were a dead giveaway.

Building trust in the minds of one's suppliers means first providing them with good visibility of the future. This means valid schedules, good forecasts, open lines of communication, and working together to establish a true win-win atmosphere between vendor and manufacturer. It also means assuring a vendor that as long as they meet the needs of the purchaser's delivery schedules and conform to the quality requirements, they will have that company's business.

The kind of close relationship necessary to accomplish this mutually beneficial alliance cannot be done with a vendor base in the thousands. The logistics and time it would take is too prohibitive. Xerox recognized this when they began their Just-in-Time program. Being a company that purchases 80 percent of their parts from outside sources, Xerox used to have almost 5000 vendors worldwide. They believed that this multiple sourcing assured them of having what they needed, just in case. They soon realized that trying to develop a positive working relationship with 5000 different companies was virtually impossible. So they proceeded to reduce and reduce and reduce their vendor base to a manageable level. They are now down to a vendor base of approximately 300, and they're not done yet.

In Chapter 10, we will explain this process by which companies have worked with their vendors. We will see both the techniques and the results that come from having a well-groomed vendor base, and why this is essential for Just-in-Time.

People, quality in the plant, and having the right system to provide valid schedules are the three primary ingredients necessary to make Just-in-Time soar. But there are also a number of other elements of

Just-in-Time that may or may not apply to every company. These factors include reducing order quantities and machine setups, and cellular manufacturing. There are also two other components necessary for Just-in-Time: system software and measurement systems.

REDUCING ORDER QUANTITIES AND SETUP REDUCTIONS

If the objective of Just-in-Time is the elimination of waste, then every time you touch a product to move it, build more than necessary, store it, or lose a minute when you're not building it, then you're still adding waste. One prominent area where this becomes blatantly clear is with large order quantities and their fundamental cause—machine setup time.

Doctor Shigeo Shingo defines setup time as the elapsed time between making "the last good part #1 to the first good part #2."

In most American manufacturing environments the time it takes to set up a machine has been accepted as a given. This allotted time was specified as a fixed cost compared against the cost of having inventory. This equation specifies how many pieces have to be made in order to produce the most economic order quantity. If it took eight hours to set up a machine to run a particular part, you needed large order quantities because you couldn't afford to make the same part more frequently. (See Figure 2-1.)

What the Japanese have said is *"challenge everything."* Why accept setup time as a given? With the help of Shigeo Shingo, they developed a process called Single Minute Exchange of Die, or SMED. This process says all setups should take under ten minutes. Ten minutes? Madness! SMED said, "not madness, intelligence." If you can get setup times to approach zero time, order quantities can approach one. You could then make whatever your immediate requirements were.

They went to the experts, the machine operators, to find out how they could make these changeover periods shorter and more efficient. They then brought in engineers to work with the operators.

Not too surprisingly, the time barriers began to shatter. By reducing setup time, they were able to reduce order quantities, which meant work-in-process inventories could be lowered, lead times began to shrink, cycle time was reduced, and feedback of quality problems was quicker so quality improved.

How our American companies approached setup reductions will be discussed in Chapter 5, but suffice it to say that they too have set

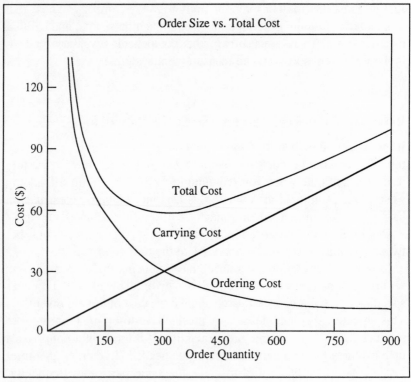

Figure 2-1.   Economic Order Quantity

benchmarks of under ten minutes. As Shingo would say, "that's not good enough."

CELLULAR MANUFACTURING

Cellular manufacturing is another of our specific ingredients which must be evaluated by each company to determine whether it's appropriate for their process. Basically, cellular manufacturing is a process of bringing together machinery and work stations that work on the same parts or products. The process is often equated with group technology, but technically, cellular manufacturing is the linking of machines and operations to produce a part, whereas group technology is primarily concerned with the production of like parts, grouped by design. Cellular manufacturing has proved to be an excellent candidate for shrinking transit times, eliminating queues, and subsequently lowering lead times. It also has a direct effect on the scheduling and routing files, simplifying them and eliminating much of the associated paperwork. The cellular approach is also an effective technique for reducing floor space, often by as much as 30 percent. (See Figure 2-2 and Figure 2-3.)

A third outcome of cellular manufacturing, and another specifically applied ingredient for Just-in-Time, has been the flattening of the bills of material. With operations and machines linked, parts and subassemblies are now directly routed into final assembly. They are no longer treated as different part numbers in the bill, so the levels of the bill of material are subsequently diminished. Again, the idea is to simplify wherever possible. Since the various processes, parts, and materials are now being linked, it means quick throughput, less paperwork, and less waste. This also translates to simplifying the planning and scheduling of parts. There are fewer parts to move, and transitions between operations are also more efficient.

In Chapter 9 we will examine how companies like Steelcase and Black and Decker approached their cellular manufacturing efforts. We will see how these changes have effectively shortened in-transit times. We will also look at some of the other benefits which arise when these processes are implemented.

SOFTWARE

In today's complex manufacturing world there is a real need for software and a computer to realize the full benefits of Just-in-Time, though it is not essential to get started. Nonetheless, no one who has successfully implemented Just-in-Time is saying that it is a way to rid themselves from the rigors of computerization. It's just not so. Even the Toyota Motor Company is an intensive user of computers, despite its wide use of manual kanban cards. Needless to say, if a computer is in use, running the right software with the right capabilities is an important ingredient necessary to augment a successful Just-in-Time implementation.

In Chapter 12 we will explore the specific requirements demanded by a Just-in-Time environment. We will take into account those ingredients and abilities that are an absolute necessity, as well as those that would be a decided plus.

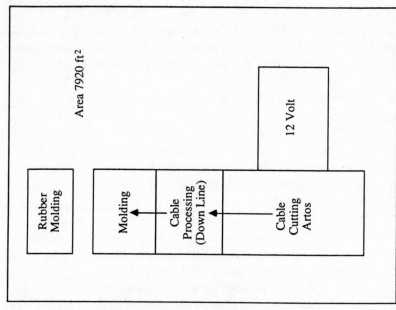

Figure 2-3.   Material Flow Diagram After Linking

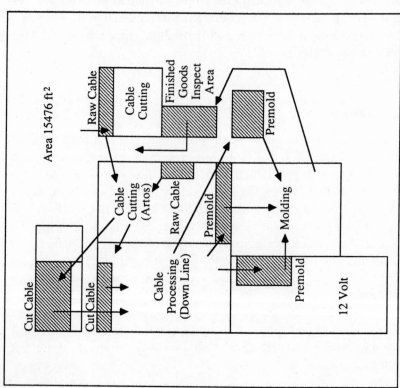

Figure 2-2.   Material Flow Diagram Before Linking

MEASUREMENTS

Just-in-Time also has a profound impact on places other than the shop floor, specifically in the area of measurement. How does a company's accounting department deal with the strains of daily deliveries, overhead absorptions, and component cost? These are just a few of the concerns that could send an accountant screeching into the night. But as we will see in Chapter 13, Just-in-Time can even reach down into the detailed figurings of accountants, simplifying and improving as it goes. Additionally, we'll also be considering some new measurements for factory performance.

THE TOTAL COMPANY ENTERPRISE

Just-in-Time is a company-wide effort, which in its totality may seem completely overwhelming. The secret to approaching this vast enterprise is to begin small. But most importantly, begin.

There is a sign on an office wall at Steelcase that says:

There are three groups of people.

1. Those who *make* things happen.
2. Those who *watch* things happen.
3. Those who wonder *what* happened.

Just-in-Time is an approach that makes people want to be in the first group. It encourages people to make things happen, rewards them, and makes the quality of life of those people who do infinitely better.

The Just-in-Time approach begins with the creation of an atmosphere conducive to getting the best from people, and it excels in helping to maintain that atmosphere.

Chapter 3

Building a Just-in-Time Environment

"WE HAVE FOUND THE ENEMY AND HE IS US."
(*Pogo*, Walt Kelley)

"WE HAVE FOUND THE ENEMY, AND IT IS WASTE."
(Just-in-Time)

When Walt Kelley's Pogo pronounced those simple words it drew knowing laughs from all who read it. We are often our own worst enemy. The same philosophical wisdom from which sprang those immortal words also gave us this: "We is faced with an insurmountable opportunity."

American manufacturing is face to face with an "insurmountable opportunity," presented by the challenge of global competition. The solution is not a radical shift to something new and different but a return to the basic techniques underlying the manufacturing process, and doing them better. The question is, Where to start? Does a company begin attacking this opportunity in those areas causing them the most pain? Does a company have to have excellent quality, planning, and scheduling before it can even begin?

Just-in-Time really goes on-line, under full power, only when the barriers between manufacturing, engineering, sales, and finance are knocked down. It really doesn't matter where a company begins its Just-in-Time program. It can be started just about anywhere and at any level in the organization, and benefits will be seen. But for Just-in-Time to really be hitting on all cylinders, every aspect of a manufacturing company has to be part of the environment.

Companies that excel at Just-in-Time have found that regardless of where they started, in order to obtain its full value there must first be a fertile and flexible environment for it to flourish and grow. The attitude of continuous improvement must be prevalent throughout the organization.

That does not necessarily imply that the Just-in-Time environment is something that needs to begin at the top of an organization and work its way down. The first phases of Just-in-Time can begin just about any place in the plant. In fact, many Just-in-Time programs have begun with middle management and a small pilot project as a way to gather evidence to show senior management what Just-in-Time can do. But to succeed on a company-wide level, top management needs to come on-line at some point and become actively involved. They are the creators of the work environment. They set the course. They may assign responsibilities, but they remain ultimately responsible for the overall tone of the business.

Initiating Just-in-Time in a manufacturing company can be as simple as using what is already available, better. There will be some benefits gained just by improving maintenance, cleaning up the shop, and exploring areas like setup reduction or material flow.

It is probably not too surprising that a company's leadership is often the place where the greatest changes need to take place. Many manufacturing companies tend to be top-down, semiautocratic organizations where there isn't a great deal of team problem solving involving front-line supervision and operators, those most affected by the changes. Just-in-Time demands involvement from all levels, from top to bottom and back up. Therefore, it is important for management to open itself to include the lower levels in the decision-making and problem-solving areas. These people are the experts at their jobs, and may know best how to address the problems at hand. (See Figure 3-1.)

At first, some managers may find it difficult to accept the idea of listening to operators' suggestions. This could be caused by a number of factors. In the past these managers may have found that worker suggestions were unrealistic, that they weren't thoroughly thought out. They could be a stickler for procedures, and feel that the idea hasn't gone through the proper channels, bypassing the chain of command. Or it could even be they feel that having top management listen to an hourly worker's idea was wasting valuable management time.

If these reasons sound familiar, it doesn't mean you won't be able to begin a Just-in-Time operation. It simply means that if you think Just-in-Time is something that will be good for your company, you may have to begin a small trial project before convincing top management. When trying to establish a new environment, one that is open

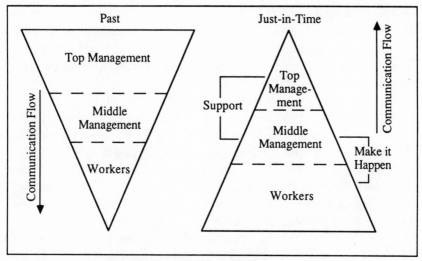

Figure 3-1. Decision-Making and Problem-Solving

and conducive to change, there is often a real reluctance to make what some may consider "radical" shifts in policy. These feelings can often be effectively dealt with through education and by the initial results that come from getting the facility in shape. When a company makes certain their employees understand what they need to do and why, it provides the process with a solid basis for success.

BUILDING TRUST

The most important aspect of an environment that is flexible, open to change and improvement, is a strong sense of trust. If people don't trust and understand what's happening, they will be determined to defeat it. This is particularly important in a company running Just-in-Time, because changes tend to happen on so many different levels at the same time. One way to help build trust is for upper management to be consistent with what it says. If they preach good quality but at the end of the month waive quality requirements for products, they're sending mixed messages. Those working in the plant have to be able to recognize that the company is willing to do things right, even if it means being late.

The companies with which we spoke agreed that management has to demonstrate to their employees that they respect them. Those in charge know that nobody comes to work to make scrap. They know their people want to do what is right. They must demonstrate it! What they will also find is there is some enlightened self-interest here, because Just-in-Time gives *everybody* an opportunity to improve their process in concert with everybody else.

One of the shining attributes of a Just-in-Time environment is the ability to get all departments involved, not simply with themselves but in context of how they service everyone else in the organization. Divisions in a manufacturing company have in the past been described as a group of islands. There's the design engineering island, the purchasing island, the manufacturing and marketing islands. Each island goes about their dedicated tasks, all driven by the same objectives of producing a good product, at a good price, with good customer service. The problem is that none of those islands have much of an idea how what they do impacts somebody else in the island chain.

If a company realizes they've been handling things badly and decides they are going to change the way they manage, they need to address the effect their decision will have on the people working there. Changing from a system of separate operations to a more integrated one is a giant step to promoting Just-in-Time.

However, changing the environment is of little help if management is unable to institute those changes effectively. For example, if an edict comes down that all employees must attend quality circle meetings each week as a way to improve communication, but no guidelines or facilitator training is provided, the quality circles will probably not produce a positive result. People in all levels of an organization have to be taken through the process so they understand what the company is trying to do, how it will affect them, and how they will be expected to change. This means management has to have the trust of their employees. This is also why a Just-in-Time environmental change can begin without the initial buy-in of upper management. A middle manager with the trust of his workers can, with almost no monetary investment, launch a Just-in-Time salvo by doing some education and training and simply getting his particular part of the house in order. There is nothing subversive or underhanded about this activity. It is a manager managing his department. But in order to succeed, the manager needs to have the trust of his people.

We will look at some other factors later that can help build trust. These ideas include no-layoff policies where applicable, workers sharing in the rewards of increased productivity, and knowing that the company will recognize a job well done.

Just-in-Time can begin anywhere in a manufacturing concern, but because of the importance of the trust issue, the sequence which companies that have successfully implemented Just-in-Time have observed is to begin with the people issues, then plant, then the systems.

The reasoning behind this is sound. By involving the people first, a company prepares everyone for the changes to come. Employees will understand the needs and goals of the program and begin to focus on their role in the upcoming process. This allows the proper environment in order to change the plant. Finally, you change the systems. The adage holds true, you change reality first, then the systems. Once the people and plant issues are being addressed, then it's time to rework the operating systems to keep up with the changes.

The process starts with open lines of communication.

OPEN LINES OF COMMUNICATION

An environment that thrives on involvement hinges on its ability to communicate. Operators need to understand the importance of Just-in-Time, and how it can be a benefit to all of them. Managers, in turn, need to listen and be responsive to the operators' recommendations. The norm is to listen but reject most suggestions and record others. Offering platitudes followed by weak actions only fuels those people who are certain the changes are not going to work in the first place.

To illustrate this, let us offer two contrasting examples of how a company can respond. One company encouraged worker suggestions by rewarding the ten best suggestions they received. The best suggestion won a TV, the next nine, clock radios. These prizes were all prominently displayed in the cafeteria for all workers to see. The program was promoted in the company newspaper and on posters around the plant, but the company received only 100 suggestions from over 1600 employees. And that was accomplished only after some upper management arm twisting.

On the other hand, when several Japanese companies made the request for suggestions, they received an astronomical amount. The difference between the two approaches was that out of that great number of replies the Japanese companies received, they accepted 80 to 90 percent. The other company had inadvertently established the "suggestion rejection committee." They received 100 suggestions, but they accepted and made a big deal about only 10. It wasn't that the rejected suggestions were necessarily poor, they just weren't as good as the top 10. What they had failed to realize was that they had turned down 90. It was little wonder that six months later these managers couldn't get any more suggestions from their employees. The point was, if they had accepted 90 and turned down only ten, the next time they probably would have received 200 suggestions, and then 400.

The Tennant Company gave their employees some training in group process skills and then opened their suggestion process to group ideas. In this manner, groups of two to thirty could get together and decide on improvements in certain areas. They found that by going to a group suggestion process it not only doubled the amount of suggestions implemented to about 40 percent, but it tripled the savings being generated by those suggestions.

The Tennant Company's response to this communication from their workers was to award 20 percent of the first year's savings to the group who came up with a new plan. In one case the savings totaled nearly $69,000, $13,700 of which ended up in the hands of those workers who communicated their ideas. Needless to say, when they established a program that said, "We not only want your suggestions, but we'll share the savings with you," their workers began to trust management's plan and do all they could to make it work.

But monetary rewards for improved communication are not the only payoff that motivates and builds trust. Simple and swift action on an idea can demonstrate a company's commitment to beginning a new order. At Black and Decker's Tarboro, North Carolina, facility the plant manager spends about half his day on the shop floor. Workers have been encouraged to stop him and tell him what is on their minds. When a suggestion from Black and Decker's storeroom supervisor was made on how to improve their material movement process, they set to it immediately. By the end of the day the idea was on its way to being implemented.

The need for focused communication lines is not only of concern between management and labor, it is important that communication exist within management as well. This receptivity to open communication within top management becomes the beacon by which the rest of the operation is to be guided. Executive committees, Just-in-Time action implementation committees, and planning and steering committees need to be formed among the ranks of upper management. These are critical to help dispel the skepticism that may arise from the lower levels.

If people don't trust that the leaders at the top are serious about making changes, they have no incentive to sign up. Just-in-Time is leadership by example, and teamwork by design. Action speaks.

These same open lines of communication also need to be established with suppliers. As with employees, suppliers also need to have a sense of trust in order to work on a Just-in-Time basis with their customers. Vendor visibility and flexibility are also essential ingredients. Xerox's two-year program to consolidate their vendor base was a long-term effort to establish real cooperative business relationships, and to markedly improve their vendor's performance, which would have been impossible with 5000 suppliers. The key here was open and trustworthy communication. As Xerox admits, this was not always the way they treated their suppliers in the past. It took time for them to assure their suppliers that they were serious about making Just-in-Time work.

Once a company begins to realize the importance of opening up their various communication channels, they are ready for the second step in laying the groundwork for a successful Just-in-Time environment. This step will bring even more people on board.

DON'T PLAN IT TO DEATH. START SMALL.

That's Hewlett-Packard's approach. "Show me it can be done." Even the most reluctant CEO will take notice when a pilot project—a small, controlled application—is started through the impetus of either middle or lower management and it starts to take off. People believe a lot more when they can see a project working. They feel even better when it's actually saving the company money.

The other aspect of this idea is that getting started doesn't become an exercise in "protection planning." People often refuse to take a real step forward because they're afraid it's going to be wrong. A manager must make sure that *paralysis through analysis* doesn't set in and kill a project before it starts. The idea is to change: do something, somewhere.

Sometimes it is best to follow the idea set forth in *In Search of Excellence*: "Ready, Fire, Aim." This is an expression that says to try something first, then adjust it if it doesn't work. You fire, and correct your aim after you've seen where the first volley lands. Then take the next step once you've got your headings. In the case of Just-in-Time, that step is to begin a pilot project.

PICK A NO-LOSE TEST AREA

The ideal place to launch Just-in-Time is in an area that is small and ripe for improvement. Nothing in the rules says you can't stack the odds in your favor. By taking this kind of approach, it limits the amount of danger that can be incurred while you're testing the water. It also makes progress obvious. For this reason the place to start, according to Charlene Adair of Hewlett-Packard, should have:

1. High visibility in the plant.
2. Be representative of the kinds of work being done in the plant.
3. Have no major production problems.
4. Be an area that has a high likelihood for success.

A number of companies have found that an excellent place to begin their pilot program is one where the greatest need exists. But wherever a company starts, pilot programs are essential. The reason is simple: Starting any new venture can be the beginning of some very trying times. By starting small you limit the scale of problems that can arise. It also allows the company the time to properly assess the benefits of Just-in-Time in this new environment. What they may find, as Bently Nevada did, was that they might need to think about redesigning their product so that it could be built in a company-wide Just-in-Time environment.

Pilots also offer an opportunity to bring on board some people who are not completely convinced the idea will work. Black and Decker put some of their most anti-Just-in-Time people in charge of their pilot program in their power cord department. These people thought that what the company wanted was an impossibility. But they went ahead. Within a few days of start-up they began seeing the first inklings of success. By the time the project was fully implemented, those people who went in with negative feelings came out as the staunchest supporters of the system.

Had Black and Decker just sent in an engineer and the plant manager and said, "This is what we want done," it would never have worked as well. But by involving the department supervisor and the operators, it became their project. It was something for which they could be proud. It gave them a sense of ownership. It was also something that made everyone else in the plant take notice.

By demonstrating Just-in-Time in action, people start to line up. They want to understand what's going on, they want to be part of the change.

Where a company implements a pilot project is important, but the real key is starting small. It doesn't take a lot of money. It takes a little understanding, a little desire, and a bit of freedom for those people trying to put it in place.

Hewlett-Packard's Vancouver division began its Just-in-Time program with a single item in a single department. The first step they took in beginning this process was to educate their people. They needed to let them know what tools were available for their use. Because of the limited size of the pilot, expenses were minimal. It is important to note, too, that most companies found the initial costs of implementing a Just-in-Time program were next to nothing. The reason for this is that the changes that initially occur are process changes, doing things differently, rather than having to make capital expenses for new equipment.

ARMING THE TEAM WITH EDUCATION

As with the implementation of any new approach, there must be a vital and continual dedication to education. It is during this educational and training phase that most employees will actively join in to install the new ideas being presented. They see management's commitment to make the company run better, and they realize they have to understand the concepts.

The education process in the plant has a dual purpose. The first is:

FACT TRANSFER

These are the why's, how's, and what's of an operation. Approaching Just-in-Time, people need to know why they have to change. This usually doesn't take much. Omark showed their employees their costs and how the dollar was affecting their product's sales worldwide. This was transferring the facts of why implementing Just-in-Time was essential. But even more importantly, Omark had to teach their people how to change the process, providing them with the tools and techniques necessary to do the job. And the third aspect is transferring the knowledge of how to properly use the techniques to make the process function.

Most companies that have successfully begun a Just-in-Time program spent a good deal of time educating everyone in their company. They armed their people with some of the techniques of Just-in-Time: how to improve setups and why it was important, how to use statistical process control to improve quality, and how to link operations to improve product flow. Black and Decker provided one-day in-plant seminars, bringing in speakers to outline the concepts of Just-in-Time. Xerox offered a number of one- to three-day workshops, which all employees were expected to attend. These companies universally encouraged their managers and workers to read books like Shigeo Shingo's *Study of the Toyota Production System*, Robert W. Hall's *Zero Inventories*, and Richard J. Schonberger's *Japanese Manufacturing Techniques*. They also showed videotapes like those produced by Hewlett-Packard's Greely division. They offered all of this as input designed to encourage and stimulate further ideas.

It is important to stress that this *Fact Transfer* is not limited to managers and operators but includes top management as well. When people hear that the general manager is going through a training and education process, they start to realize this is something for everybody. Nobody is too big or small to learn.

The second purpose of an educational system is:

BEHAVIOR CHANGE

This occurs when people really understand why and how Just-in-Time works. They feel confident in their knowledge of what their role is in the process and have become convinced of the need to do their jobs differently. The *behavior change* also sets in when operators really can see that management is serious about their own participation. This is where people begin to realize their ownership in the process—when engineers seek out the ideas of operators, and when marketing willingly joins in sales forecasting and the master scheduling process because they recognize it as a way to give better customer service, increase sales volume, and make the company more competitive. It is also the time when people begin aggressively making things happen because they are confident in their knowledge, rather than passively sitting back still unsure that this "new idea" is the way to go.

In order to completely accomplish this kind of change in the company mind-set, certain criteria must be met:

1. Active participation of top management in the education process.
2. Peer confirmation.
3. Line accountability for education.
4. Total immersion of key people.
5. Continuing reinforcement.
6. Credibility.
7. Enthusiasm.

Active top management leadership and participation in the education process. The need to involve top management in this change process is absolute. If top management fails to be educated, and most specifically the general manager, all below the general manager who take their cues from him are going to feel a mixed message is being sent. On the other hand, if the general manager is properly educated and demonstrates how important he believes the process is, everybody else down the organizational chart will as well.

A company can't possibly succeed in implementing a new approach in which those in charge don't understand themselves. The leadership in a Just-in-Time movement has to be *informed*, and that can only come through education.

Bently Nevada's Ray Bacon began sending a steady stream of books and articles to his general manager to bring him into the process. Eventually, the general manager began asking for more of these "executive briefings," and Bacon gladly responded. With the general manager fully on board, Bently Nevada employees had a clear signal from the top about the importance of continuing education.

Peer Confirmation. Peer confirmation is essential to build confidence in the success of the project. This is the bulletproofing process that allows people to feel comfortable with what they know and which then allows ownership to take place. Whenever a large organization proposes a major shift in the way things are done, a bell curve of response can be drawn. On one end are those who are wildly enthusiastic, and on the other, those who are completely negative. In the middle are the vast majority who want to believe, but are passively resisting the change until they feel certain of what to do and how to do it. They don't want to mess things up.

Peer confirmation gives all people, from top to bottom, the ability to share their knowledge, compare notes, and use each other as a sounding board for taking necessary shots at these new ideas. This helps assure people the ideas make sense and can stand up to criticism. Education in this sense is sharing with others until they are able to integrate those concepts into their own lexicon. This process of exchange builds confidence. It lowers the level of uncertainty and anxiety; it raises the level of success; it builds ownership. It enables people to see the need to change the way they do their jobs.

Whenever a process of gaining knowledge begins, a fear factor is also set in motion. As the first bits of knowledge start to be understood, the fear level rises. This is because the persons can now clearly see the problems, but as yet they haven't learned the solutions. Proceeding with the knowledge process, a person gains a better understanding of how to fix the problems, and the fear factor lowers substantially. The important thing is to push through and overcome the initial fear factors. Doing this builds a high level of confidence and fires up people to move aggressively ahead.

Line accountability for education. This is the process of teaching those people who will make it work, showing them how to use the tools, and getting them to believe they can make the tools work as a team. An education program must be structured so that a specific group of people can be held accountable for making certain that the people are properly educated. These are the department heads and the operating managers of the business. They're the only ones who can legitimately be held accountable for success in their areas.

Total immersion for key people. Those managers who will facilitate this process of change need to make the changes their own. This is an intensive educational immersion in the process to equip them with the techniques to make this transfer of information work.

Continuing reinforcement. Oliver Wight said it well: "Grease gun education doesn't work." What he was referring to was the "one-shot, quick-fix" educational approach, which has rarely met with any great success. Knowledge gained without further reinforcement evaporates like water left in a pan. Continual reinforcement improves retention, sharpens operational details, and can help answer questions that may arise later. To avoid dissipating this understanding it becomes essential for education to be a continuing growth process rather than a quick shot.

Communication and dialogue are the essential ingredients. People need to feel they can discuss, ask questions, get answers, focus on issues, and get specific. This, in turn, brings these education sessions to life. They become involving, as well as reassuring, because people begin to see through these interactions to how the process can be put to use.

Credibility. Anyone can transfer facts, but to change behavior, people need to feel that those handling the educational process really know and understand their particular situation. This credibility in the eyes of those receiving information is an essential ingredient to build trust and to get by the fear factors that will invariably arise. As a result, use your veterans, not your rookies.

Enthusiasm. In order for new ideas to spread, enthusiasm is a must. In this case enthusiasm is not really a criteria for behavior change but a barometer of change. If a company fulfills the other criteria, it will generate enthusiasm. If enthusiasm is not being generated, something is not right with the other factors. This is not to be confused with the rah-rah variety of enthusiasm that quickly burns itself out at the first opportunity, but one where confidence and conviction become the drive to make things better. Behavior change takes place when you know the right tools for the job are present. It makes the job both easier and more enjoyable, and that too generates enthusiasm.

As with the aspects of communication, education is also an area that companies have opened up to their vendors. The idea is that the more everyone knows, the better the process will flow. Xerox is one of the acknowledged leaders in this area, with their excellent supplier education program. Though this will be discussed in greater detail in Chapter 10, it is important to emphasize that the steps taken to educate the company need to be extended to the outside vendors as well.

PUT THE USERS IN CHARGE

By putting the users in charge, knowledge and trust join together to produce teamwork. This is a time when bridges are built between the separate manufacturing islands, and when barriers between manufacturing, engineering, materials, sales and finance are broken down.

It is when a company actually puts the users in charge, and makes appropriate staff people members of the team, not leaders, that marks the melding of a culture ready to succeed with Just-in-Time. It says the company respects the value of all its employees, and wants them to work together. When accountability and responsibility are vertically integrated throughout an organization, top to bottom, it makes everyone part owner in the process. Suddenly, things take on a new dimension, and productivity is a direct and positive payoff.

The object is to establish common goals—it's how many can we build as a team, working like a team. William Ouchi, author of *Theory Z*, went so far as to say that "Nothing of consequence occurs as a result of individual effort. Everything important in life happens as a result of teamwork or collective effort." This is quite a contrast to the "What's in it for me!" attitude that has often prevailed in most businesses.

Gary Vredenberg at Steelcase has found that Just-in-Time does push the team approach over the individual. Interestingly, he is still seeing the same kinds of objectives being met as he did when things were handled more individually. The difference, noted by Vredenberg, is that the success rate of the projects using the team approach is much higher, and the implementation period is shorter because the project belongs to the people doing the work.

There are a number of sound, fundamental principles why the small-team approach is so effective. It allows people to exchange and share their expertise. The dynamics of the group offers a forum for criticizing and bullet-proofing ideas. Work can be divided among the participants according to expertise. The team also brings a collective ownership to any project worked on together, which provides strength and support for the work being done. Finally, out of the team concept comes agreement. Team members realize the interdependence that must exist to execute a project.

This is the same as playing football as a team or playing as a group of individuals. A good team player worries about the guy across the line from him, instead of his teammates on his right and left. "They're going to do the job, and I'm prepared to do mine." This same attitude is what it takes to succeed as a team in manufacturing.

CHOOSING TEAMS

By following the steps laid out here, the environment has evolved to a point where the people have the educational tools they need, and they can now step forward and integrate their expertise into the process.

At Tektronix's Unicorn Division in Wilsonville, Oregon, teams were formed that included schedulers, stock handlers, planners, buyers, assemblers, and technicians. If there were problems or if something was going wrong, these teams met to iron out the wrinkles. They quickly learned how their work impacted everyone else, allowing a stock handler to understand what a planner's needs are, and vice versa. Once that was done they could work out their problems much more easily.

Years ago there were a rash of meetings such as these. They were held under the banner of quality circles. They blossomed like a field of poppies, brilliant in their presentation but for the most part short-lived. Though some companies were able to maintain the integrity of their quality circles, most died for lack of support.

What caused their demise? First, many companies saw quality circles as a quick fix. When results were slow to come interest waned. Second, circle leaders were basically untrained in the dynamics of group facilitation. They simply did not know how to direct the interaction necessary to make these programs really work. Finally, when it came time to act on the suggestions, management found itself between a rock and a hard place—that is, do they actively support high quality, or do they make shipments?

Because many quality circle programs failed does not mean that the idea was bad, merely the execution was off. Just-in-Time attacks the execution problems head on. Simultaneously, quality circles are re-emerging to feed what had not been in place before.

This open exchange of ideas has been especially profitable in areas that link engineering and manufacturing. In some companies an engineer, looking for improvements, might come out onto the shop floor and monitor the manufacturing process. Workers would suggest design or process changes, and the engineer might then go back to his drafting table and incorporate them. But as companies grew and subsequently the demands on engineers also increased, they began losing contact with the shop floor. Engineers were often forced to design the product without first-hand knowledge of how the person in the factory was going to have to make it.

Then, when the operator came to the engineer with a problem, the engineer was rarely enthusiastic about listening, believing the operator didn't understand the reasoning behind the design. Just-in-Time doesn't allow that kind of separation. An engineer has to see himself as a resource to help solve an operator's problems. That is how products are made better and more efficiently.

As Hewlett-Packard's Judy Oberg explained the initial development of one of their printers, "the design and R&D teams were very closely involved with manufacturing, learning the concepts and then making sure the products they brought back were manufacturable in the environment." *Engineering must provide designs for manufacturable products.*

Bently Nevada's vice president of Manufacturing, Ray Bacon, points out that they operate in a similar manner. It was for this reason they moved the offices of their printed circuit board designers right next to the production line. They also were able to work with their design engineers to give up some space on the PC board for the inclusion of an internal testing device. As we shall see in Chapter 9, this decreased testing time and reduced Bently Nevada's lead time significantly.

Steelcase's Joe Lauria, superintendent of their File Machine Division, believes part of the secret of breaking down resistance between engineering and manufacturing is to involve people on both sides early on in the process.

Lauria recalls a time when he asked two hourly people at Steelcase to put together a work cell. It was a project which would eventually affect about thirty people. He could have gone onto the floor and told his workers he had consulted with industrial engineering and they now wanted to make some changes. Those changes would have been made, but as he explained, "it would be like pulling teeth to get all the people to buy it. This way we put a couple of hourly people in charge and said, 'you two guys take a look at this and you tell us the way to do it.' "

"They were in charge," Lauria continues, "And when the program began to roll all the rest of the people pitched right in. They could talk back and forth to each other because they were working on the same product. They could also make changes. When they said, 'We've got to have help,' an engineer was sent out, and he, in effect, took the information from these guys according to their needs." Lauria then put this idea into perspective. "Since these workers shared in the decision making process, and because they were also responsible for making it work, they had a much greater sense of pride in how all of it falls into place."

One of the things Omark saw in Japan that made particular sense to them was the Japanese had only *engineers* working at their plants. There was no distinction made between design engineers, industrial engineers, or manufacturing engineers. Today, Omark is trying to emulate that idea, of not drawing such a fine line in their own engineering departments.

A primary element of Hewlett-Packard's Just-in-Time process is that if a worker on the line has a quality problem, he stops the line. He turns on a signal and a supervisor immediately gets involved. If the problem can't be solved and requires engineering attention, the supervisor can call an engineer to determine what the problem is and the line will remain shut down.

Needless to say, it was quite a cultural shift for those engineers to come down on the floor to solve problems when they happened. But once they understood that under Just-in-Time, when the line was shut down they were in fact shutting down the whole factory, they changed quickly. The engineers even left their home phone numbers so they could be called at night if a problem surfaced during the second shift. Hewlett-Packard knew that kind of engineering support was essential to keep the program functioning.

To emphasize the importance of their engineers' involvement, and to have a little fun, when an engineer is called onto the shop floor to solve a problem at H-P's Vancouver plant, a fireman's hat with a flashing red light awaits the rescuing troubleshooter. It's another way to help break down some of the barriers between engineering and manufacturing. It also helps maintain the level of enthusiasm necessary to provide good teamwork.

A manufacturing atmosphere where design engineers are expected to be part of the team, not sequestered away from the action, gives them a sense of responsibility for achieving the goals that are common to every employee of the company—making the best product, at the best price, on time.

At H-P's Vancouver Division these figures speak well for the kinds of results that can be obtained with good teamwork:

Work-in-process inventory dollars	down 82%
Floorspace	down 40%
Scrap/rework	down 30%
Product build time	down 85%
Labor efficiency	up 50%
Shipments	up 20%

Since Just-in-Time reaches into every corner of a manufacturing environment, Just-in-Time teams need to be equally widespread. Steelcase presently has more than seventy-five different teams made up of volunteers, working on things from designing work cells to making sure that instruction sheets are getting to shipping.

The essence of these teams should be to "make the familiar strange." In other words, team members should look at things that they are used to, things they see everyday, and imagine they've just landed in the environment from another planet. Then they should ask, "Why are we doing it this way?"

Just-in-Time is continually looking for better ways to do the same old things. Only with Just-in-Time every same old thing has to pass muster before it is allowed to remain. This is the driver of Just-in-Time, the continual push to be better.

These same Just-in-Time cultural rules hold true in dealing with suppliers as well. Even though almost all the companies we spoke with agreed that their Just-in-Time programs began by getting their own house in shape first, it is critical for a company to address the needs of their vendors' environment too.

Xerox has been leading the way in bringing their vendors on board for Just-in-Time. According to Xerox's Pierre Landry, they believe that early supplier involvement really pays off. Xerox's attitude is to show them everything and let them have real visibility of the operation.

To help their vendors make the transition to Just-in-Time, Xerox, as previously mentioned, offers their suppliers an education program that begins with a one-day seminar for the vendor's senior management. Then there is a three-day seminar for three of a supplier's middle managers. Invited to this seminar would be a manufacturing engineer, a manufacturing person, and a quality person. Xerox then sends some of their own people out to the vendor's plant to help on-site.

Some of the benefits Xerox has received from their vendors after making them part of the team have been greatly improved quality, a 50 percent reduction in product cost, and shorter lead times. We will see more of Xerox's vendor dealings in Chapter 10. For now, it is important to note that adapting a company's culture to a Just-in-Time methodology also means leading by example. This translates into the need for a company to actively help a supplier adapt their culture to fit both parties' needs.

What we have been building here is an environment that has reached deeply into all levels of a company. What we must remember, though, is we began the process by starting small. Like any procreative act, the process of creating a culture can and does multiply and grow rapidly. What makes this rapid growth possible is the next step for constructing a Just-in-Time environment.

BUILD ON SUCCESS

When setting out on a new direction, there is no confidence builder greater than initial success. Ask any rookie pitcher coming up to the big leagues who struck out the first batter he faced, and you'll hear about the fundamental importance of a small success. The same is true in manufacturing. When a company has some initial successes with Just-in-Time, let the world know.

The point is that skeptics become believers when they see good results. Success sells. It also builds confidence. One important factor to remember is that in order to determine results, measurements must be taken before, during, and after the pilot. By documenting everything through journals, charts, photos, and videotapes, everyone can see who made the project work, how they did it, and why it succeeded. The Tennant Company let everyone know about their workers' successes in their pilot program and touted the shared savings. Immediately people around the plant became infected with the fever to get going in their own areas.

Black and Decker's first results were so successful and obvious that the word of their success was spreading even before the official company-wide heralding. It was interesting, though, that few people heard about the snags encountered. *There are always going to be glitches,* but by working in teams, those problems are usually solved without destroying the spirit, and often in a manner that uses the most common sense.

"When you are all done," says the man who put together Black and Decker's pilot program, "if it all doesn't look as if you should have done it years ago, it may not be the right solution." In other words, it's truly back to the basics.

"Some of our solutions," concurs Steelcase's Burch, "were indeed very simple. We turned our people on. We got a groundswell of ideas. The workers were the hidden resource at Steelcase. What they came up with when we opened up the lines of communication was one part common sense, that is, making things simpler; and one part technical, that is, involving equipment, layout, setups, handling, and scheduling."

Ah, but there is a caution. This isn't some Polyannaish approach where the Just-in-Time world is always wonderful. There is no wonderful wizard of Just-in-Time that magically elevates companies above the potholes on the yellow brick road. A company beginning this Just-in-Time journey must deal with one final element.

RECOGNIZING THE OPPORTUNITIES

When problems surface, and they will, impeding the process flow, a company must have certain fundamentals firmly in place in order to address these problems, turning them into opportunities. For example, no amount of workers' ingenuity and dedication can overcome the lack of good tools. Although possible benefits may come from using existing tools better, the correct solution requires having the right ones to do the job.

The responsibility coming down from the top, though, is to also recognize the rocks before they sink the ship. The saying "an ounce of prevention" is not to be ignored. By focusing on these issues, and addressing the large problems that break the surface (you don't have to see more than the tip of an iceberg to know there's plenty more below), managers can work with employees to remove these impediments and improve the process flow.

The right tools have to be available. No one would expect a surgeon to do a good job in open-heart surgery with a chainsaw. A company has to supply their people with the right tools to get the job done. This applies to all three aspects of a manufacturing operation: its people, its plant, and its systems.

Once a company has the right tools, which we will discuss further in Chapters 6 through 9, it implies that they must be disciplined in their approach. As Hewlett-Packard's Charlene Adair explains H-P's direction, "There is a process for doing things, and we follow that process." If the tools are there, they need to be used, and used properly.

EVERYTHING IS JOB ONE

Isn't there one thing more important than another in starting this Just-in-Time process? No.

"There isn't a number one priority," explained Omark's Vern Pearson. "We've gotten to the point at Omark that when you talk about a priority system it really upsets people. We are undergoing so much change that for anybody to sit down and say, 'these are priorities 1 to 100,' isn't realistic. They are all critical issues we are working on. If you want, SMED (Single Minute Exchange of Die) is a number one priority because it affects quality, which is a number one priority, because it affects inventory reduction, which, yes, is a number one priority also. But you can't do any of them without people involvement.''

If everything is number one, then the issue is not where you start but that you *do* start.

At Steelcase they realized this, and though they have accomplished a great deal, they also know they still have a long way to go. ''But at least we have started,'' says Rob Burch ''We have a plan, and we know what to do, which is half the battle. A lot of times half the battle is understanding what the problem is, and knowing what you have to do to fix it.''

In a Just-in-Time environment there is direction but no destination. It is a continuing journey toward being the best. It offers a company a chance for survival in the world market. Black and Decker's Ken Good made this quite clear when he referred to the effects of their Just-in-Time program: ''Had we not been continually striving for productivity improvements, and just said, 'Hey, we're doing a good enough job, why mess with it?' I really don't believe we'd be in business today. We've hung on where a lot of other plants have gone by the wayside.''

SUMMARY

Building a culture that supports the needs of *the plant of the present* demands a combination of a thinking worker, a listening supervisor, a supportive manager, and inspiring leadership. These aren't newly invented ideas. These are, in fact, aspects that most companies have felt were always important. Just-in-Time offers a fresh opportunity to say again, *''This is important!''* But it does so with some prescribed and tested steps to integrating these ideas into deeds. Dreaming of a better way is the vision; making a better way is the action. Just-in-Time is action based on clear vision.

A much closer examination of all the specific elements of Just-in-Time will follow, including how some of the best companies in America have made Just-in-Time a solution for getting their operations in top shape. The journey continues.

Chapter 4

The Thinking Worker— The Secret Weapon

"98% OF THE BATTLE IS LISTENING AND PAYING ATTENTION. WHEN A WORKER HAS A GOOD IDEA, YOU DO SOMETHING."

ASK THE PROFESSIONAL

If you want the right answers, ask someone who spends his time working hard at what you can only conjecture. This is especially true when beginning any business venture. You want the facts.

Unfortunately, this has not always been the case on the manufacturing floor or in the office. The ones with the greatest experience here have often been the last ones to be asked anything. In fact, they usually aren't asked at all, but told. These are the machine operators, the direct-labor people, and the hourly workers, who for the most part have been seen merely as a means to an end.

Just-in-Time won't succeed with that attitude. Every aspect of the process needs to be examined to see what can be trimmed, what can be altered, and what must remain. This kind of detail makes cooperation and input from all levels absolutely necessary. It also means that the people operating on the shop floor not only have to contribute, but they also need to be recognized as a vital source of expertise at what they do.

As mentioned in Chapter 3, the people aspects of Just-in-Time are crucial to a successful implementation. For this reason, it is important to take a deeper look into these ideas, expanding those previously mentioned, while presenting some additional concepts to help open the process.

Omark has a drawing that is seen throughout the plant. It shows up on flyers, posters, and sometimes even on daily schedules. It is a rough drawing of a smiling person. The message is simple. Every employee has a brain, a mouth, and a heart. (See Figure 4-1.) Below the drawing you'll often find this: "Communicate! A shared decision is better than one that's handed down. Change should take place because the people make it happen. Get a team of people to work toward an objective—shared responsibility! Find ways to let people put their ideas into practice. Recognize accomplishments."

These are the elements of employee involvement necessary to make Just-in-Time happen. Without them, it is nothing more than a charade. For that reason, there are four words management must emblazen into their minds when fostering relationships with their employees: *Listen. Support. Recognize. Reward.*

These are the respect builders. They aren't just words, they are action. They say we treat our employees like adults. There are some company managers who have decided that they must maintain complete responsibility for their operations. Rather than trusting the capabilities of their workers, they set up a situation where adult workers are being treated in a very child-like fashion. The worker is told what to do and what not to do. There is little motivation for the worker to feel like an integral part of the overall organizational process. When workers are treated like children, there is little opportunity for a company to progress toward excellence, because they will be ignoring one of their most productive knowledge resources.

"Ninety-eight percent of the battle," says Bently Nevada's Ray Ba-

Figure 4-1

con, "is listening and paying attention. When a worker has a good idea, you do something. When they've got a legitimate complaint, you fix it. I'm firmly convinced that the only way it really works is that everybody has to be playing off the same sheet of music." In other words, every player playing in concert with everyone else. Engineers, whether design or manufacturing, can't be expected to have all the answers, nor can the worker. But by marrying the expertise of all groups, innovative and positive solutions can be developed.

It didn't take long before Bacon discovered what can happen when a company relieves some of the burden from engineering for making changes. A line worker, who had been dutifully assembling a product designed fifteen years ago and left virtually untouched since then, thought, "There's a better way to do this."

The worker then found out what he needed to do to suggest the changes. He asked engineering what the criteria were for making the change. He was told they had to test 500 of them. Then, together with his supervisor, and Bacon's help, he went ahead, made the changes, and tested it on the 500 required assemblies. The upshot: The tests proved what the worker had suspected. Bently Nevada now had a better product than they'd ever had before, and all manufacturing had to do was inform engineering they were making the change.

The notion of the thinking worker treats people with a respect for what they know, no matter where they work, no matter how much they are paid, no matter if they wear a tie to work or not. When it came to putting in a new assembly line, Steelcase knew who to ask. The people on the floor had more first-hand knowledge about how the product was built than anyone else in the plant. All they needed was a feeling that their input would be respected and acted upon. With that assured, things got done.

"We get the employee involved early in the concept stages," says Steelcase's Harvey Ringerwole. "We get all the ideas we can from them. It also lets them know what's coming around and they are very receptive."

"By sharing information with our employees," says Omark's Vern Pearson, "about sales volume, economic problems, competition, and pricing problems, it has helped tremendously to get people motivated to look for ways to improve productivity."

These issues of worker visibility and trust make Just-in-Time effective. Even though some of this information in many companies is private, the more that can be shared the better. When everyone from top management to direct labor knows the direction their company is headed, it opens the process to complete scrutiny. And when employees believe "there is nothing sacred in the plant," they're going to put their efforts and ideas forward to make it better. Why? Because they know what the company is trying to accomplish.

The Tennant Company operates under a similar creed of worker visibility and creative encouragement. When plans were first drawn to improve the operations in one of their weldment areas, industrial engineering began the task and came up with a system and plan that would do the job for about $120,000. The cost overwhelmed top management, and they wanted nothing to do with it. But a couple of years later, after giving the problem some further consideration, the operators said they thought they could do a little better. Their figure for rearranging the weldment area came in at $2,000. Top management eagerly endorsed it, and the operators made the changes.

SOLVING PROBLEMS

Walk the shop floors at Omark, Black and Decker, or Hewlett-Packard, and in every work area you find a *flip chart* containing notes and suggestions from workers. These pages will form the agenda of the various team meetings. On them are the workers' collected data on problem areas, shortages, process improvement suggestions, and interdepartmental messages. The information on these charts is tangible evidence of making partnerships out of formerly adversarial relationships. Mutually attacking the company's problems is a change that has benefited *all* of the employees.

This is not to imply that all the problems in manufacturing will be relieved by flip charts and forming better relations. There always will to be problems. Somebody will invariably be racing about putting out brushfires. Normally, this is the one aspect of manufacturing that can eat up a manager's day faster than just about anything else. The burden of running the company has always been squarely in management's lap. Now, some of the problems can be put into other trusted hands, freeing managers to manage. This is where the team meeting approach addressed in the last chapter comes directly into play.

The Tennant Company calls these groups of workers dedicated to making Just-in-Time work "SWAT" Teams. That stands for "Stop Waste At Tennant."

Despite the extremely positive results of these teams of workers, there are some difficulties that arise when beginning these teams that need to be addressed. When Steelcase began bringing their workers together, they discovered that at first some people were reluctant to take part and speak out. Being front and center with their ideas was not only new to them, it was a little scary. But when they realized that these meetings had more to do with job enhancement than public speaking, they became involved.

In fact, the people who became the most insecure at Hewlett-Packard during this switchover to more direct-labor input were the supervisors themselves. Suddenly, the problem-solving areas they had traditionally been responsible for, and for which they usually received their greatest recognition, were being shared with hourly workers.

What they had to discover was the same lesson the supervisors at Tektronix learned: that in the traditional sense, these supervisors are no longer "the bosses." They're "the coaches." As Tektronix's R. Michael Johnson explained, "It's unfortunate, but the people who got a great deal of satisfaction out of being bosses, and not coaches, probably won't succeed in a Just-in-Time environment." The important factor is getting the work done in the best possible fashion. Supporting that effort is the manager's job.

Xerox encountered a "boss" problem when they began their team process. It quickly became evident they initially has to exclude their foremen from setup reduction team meetings as they tended to dominate the proceedings. They were unable to relinquish the boss mentality. They were also the ones who were most likely to miss a meeting, which caused problems in direction, since they had been running the show. Once the operators had more control, Xerox began realizing the benefits of their team approach.

RUNNING A TEAM MEETING

As we mentioned in Chapter 3, the notion of providing proper training for leaders of team meetings is critical. This has been a void in the process which has sunk many group encounters. To assure the success of this concept, a company should find a program that professionally teaches facilitator training. Without the proper tools a leader may find himself unable to direct discussions and stimulate the members and their ideas. That the facilitator is properly prepared is particularly crucial at the first meeting of such a group. The people involved can sense these are serious meetings and not simply an afterthought. By taking a positive first step a company eliminates the risk of turning off the people they want to participate.

Proper preparation is the key. Besides some facilitator training, a Just-in-Time team leader needs to have done some subject homework as well to assure a successful first meeting. This means reading the material available on the topic, as difficult and technical as some of that may be, to provide a starting point for discussions. Unfortunately, as regards Just-in-Time, there are really very few structured materials available. Nonetheless, if the group leader can identify a specific area that needs work, some information can be found that can at least act as a launching point for group discussions.

One reason the development of the thinking worker has been so successful is peer pressure. Successfully running a Just-in-Time operation is so dependent on everyone pulling their weight that any foot-dragging is quickly revealed. Because every aspect of a manufacturing company is under scrutiny, the participation of every employee becomes essential to making the process work.

FLEXIBLE AND MULTI-SKILLED LABOR

This kind of total participation typically leads to flexibility on the part of the labor force, which translates to workers being cross-trained in a variety of operations. As we will see when we look more closely into the aspects of cellular manufacturing, worker flexibility between operations is extremely important.

One area of major concern when speaking about a flexible workforce is the involvement of unions. As with other groups in Just-in-Time, bringing the unions into the process in the beginning allows them to understand what the company is trying to accomplish. A company with whom we spoke had a union liaison on their pilot project team, so the union issues and questions were being addressed from the start.

One reason Pierre Landry believes Xerox manufacturing is still alive is due to an agreement worked out with their unions to allow them to cross-train their people. They not only communicated with the union leadership the survival factors involved, but at Xerox's expense they took the union leaders to Japan to visit with Fuji Xerox and their suppliers so they could see for themselves the nature of the competition. They came back convinced that Xerox's market position was being threatened and allowed major concessions for cross-training.

Cummins UK is another union house that has implemented Just-in-Time operations with a flexible work force. By including their unions in their process development, they devised incentive bonus programs based on worker flexibility. They called these "skill modules," and though there was some initial reluctance to this cross-training, by communicating the need and the improvements there was little cultural shock.

Like other companies, Hewlett-Packard has set an objective for all their direct-labor employees to be cross-trained. Part of this is due to their shift scheduling system, which allows workers to arrive on the first shift anytime between 6:00 AM and 7:30 AM. Their shifts can then end anywhere between 2:30 PM and 4:00 PM. An arrangement of this kind requires cross-training. At 6:00 AM there may be only one person running two work stations. Without cross-training this can be a problem when the necessary support people aren't around. In such cases, though, a flexible worker can handle either operation.

But of even greater importance than filling vacancies, cross-training allows for truly effective problem solving. A flexible worker can participate when problems arise at any point on the line, rather than just their particular operation.

An excellent example of this occurred one night at Omark. On the graveyard shift, a work station ran out of parts. The supervisor had car trouble and was late arriving. Since the workers had all been cross-trained, and encouraged to work as a thinking unit, they took matters into their own hands. They found that the problem was in the zinc plating process. They then found a worker who could get the product flowing again. The supervisor arrived to find everything in running order.

The workers at Omark were able to find the right operator because of a chart they had produced. Along the side of this gridlike matrix were listed the names of every direct-labor employee, and across the top were all the different operations in the plant. Wherever an employee had been cross-trained was checked, which meant that solving problems such as the one described above was as easy as reading down a line on a chart. (See Figure 4-2.)

Had those workers not been cross-trained, had they not been encouraged to think for themselves, the normal course would have been to sit around until a boss showed up to think for them. Just-in-Time sees this as wasteful. Motivating workers to accept responsibility, and to feel ownership in the process, becomes a crucial aspect to eliminat-

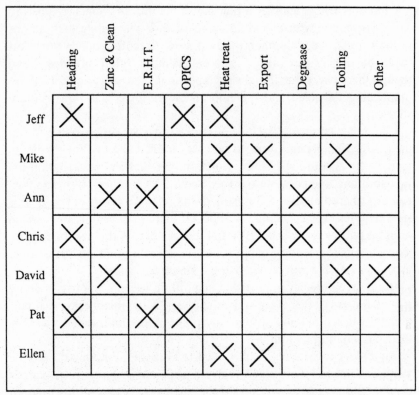

	Heading	Zinc & Clean	E.R.H.T.	OPICS	Heat treat	Export	Degrease	Tooling	Other
Jeff	X			X	X				
Mike					X	X		X	
Ann		X	X				X		
Chris	X			X		X	X	X	
David		X						X	X
Pat	X		X	X					
Ellen					X	X			

Figure 4-2. Omark Cross-Training Chart

ing the waste. The workers know it has to get done. They know what to do. So they do it!

MOTIVATION—INCENTIVE AND RECOGNITION

When Ann Owen at Black and Decker points to her operators on Black and Decker's cordless drill assembly line and tells a visitor, "These are my professionals," she does so with pride and assurance. She knows that it is through their efforts that productivity on this line has nearly doubled, and she recognizes that, respecting the work they are doing.

Motivation, incentive, and recognition are the driving force behind the success of the thinking worker and in turn make up the brain, mouth, and heart of Just-in-Time. But what motivates people to do their best? And then motivated, how does a company maintain that enthusiasm beyond the excitement of initial involvement?

Since the thrust of Just-in-Time is the journey, keeping the intensity alive and moving forward is critical. The skeptic is bound to say, "In a couple of months, Just-in-Time will fizzle out like all the rest of these programs. Complacency is sure to set in and all that enthusiasm will die. The only thing American workers care about is doing their time and getting out."

There are a number of good reasons why this argument doesn't hold up. First, companies implementing Just-in-Time are doing so with an eye on maintaining momentum. As previously mentioned, Just-in-Time is not a quick fix. It is a sustaining attitude. It's an adjustment to the manufacturing diet that is not just looking for a temporary weight loss, but permanent fitness. That means eliminating wasteful habits and continually exercising the system.

In an effort to maintain their momentum and tone, every six months Steelcase changes the makeup of its company teams. New volunteers are brought in and fresh ideas are stimulated. And since even the best of these companies admits they are a long way from total excellence, they are constantly looking toward the future. Just-in-Time is not only a look at the local environment, checking what is happening on a small scale, it is recognizing the small scale in relation to the big picture. In terms of a manufacturing company, that long-term vision centers on a work force delivering day in and day out. Motivating them is often a matter of a company saying they are going to do something and then doing it. Another form of motivation is to offer incentives.

INCENTIVE

When most people think of incentive programs, the first thing they think of is money. Once again, the skeptic will raise an eyebrow and say, "American labor is already too expensive. It's what's sending work overseas."

The notion of high labor costs has been a popular excuse for a lack of American competitiveness. It seems like such a simple answer. If you knock down the wage rate you become more competitive. It should follow then that the country with the lowest wage rate should be the most competitive, but that is not the case—witness China and India.

There is no getting around the fact that American direct-labor rates are higher than the world average. The point is, if American manufacturing can get the most out of their direct labor dollar, while working hard to manage the 90 percent of the sales dollar that goes for things other than direct labor, their competitive ability will dramatically improve. It is not the cost per *labor hour* that counts, it's the total cost per *unit*.

The way to make people more productive is not to cut salaries by 10%, but to remove the obstacles that keep those laborers from improving their productivity from 30 to 50 percent. (See Figure 4-3.) That is what Just-in-Time is all about: removing the obstacles that get in the way of productivity. But if a worker sees his productivity rising, while his wage rate remains the same, what is going to motivate him to keep working hard?

In some cases, one answer is simply having a job. Competition in many industries is so fierce that employees realize if they don't do better and get better, they'll be out of a job because the company will be out of business. But even that is not incentive enough. One characteristic often found in the companies who are making a success of Just-in-Time is that they have a profit-sharing program with their employees. Profit sharing is not paying extra wages, it is giving labor a piece of their hard work, part ownership in the process.

Steelcase has one of the country's finest profit-sharing, bonus, and benefit systems. It is true that they are the world leader in the field of making office furniture, but it's chicken and the egg time. Are they the

Sales Dollar Breakdown			
	Component Manufacturer	Equipment Manufacturer	Consumer Products Manufacturer
Labor	.11	.07	.04
Material	.28	.43	.25
Overhead	.20	.21	.10
Factory Cost	.59	.71	.39
Operating Cost	.25	.15	.40
Total Cost	.84	.86	.79
Profit	.16	.14	.21
Sales	$1.00	$1.00	$1.00

- *Component manufacturers* who make parts for other companies such as manufacturers of electric motors.
- *Equipment manufacturers* who make products like industrial machines or tractors.
- *Consumer product manufacturers* who make products like pharmaceuticals, toiletries, etc.

Figure 4-3. Sales Dollar Breakdown Chart

leader because they treat their employees well, or do they treat their employees well because they are the leaders in their field? The answer at Steelcase is the former. It has been reported in *Forbes Magazine* that Steelcase has paid bonuses to its hourly personnel that give the hourly people average salaries over $30,000.

RECOGNITION

But what was most interesting at these Just-in-Time facilities was that though the money aspects were important, they were not *the* most important worker concern. That spot was filled by *recognition*.

Kevin Donigan was one of Omark's Area Parts Controllers, an hourly worker in charge of keeping track of parts in different areas of the facility. Kevin was instrumental in helping to implement Omark's Just-in-Time program on the shop floor. When it was time to show and explain Omark's system to visitors, it was Kevin who led the way, not his plant manager. Part of his reward for the job he had done was a promotion, but what he admitted was probably his biggest reward was being able to show people the job he had helped Omark do. As he said, "The money doesn't mean as much as having your ideas used." It comes down to feeling a part of the process—knowing that you've got a job, that you are contributing, and most importantly that you are being properly recognized by the company for the job you are doing.

The issue of employee recognition was stressed at every company we visited. The Tennant Company, for example, had charts and displays up on their bulletin boards heralding the success of their various Just-in-Time programs. Each display explained how the project worked, but the majority of space on the display was taken up with the pictures and names of the workers who made it happen. The same was true with a video presentation they produced to show other people and companies how the Tennant Company had put Just-in-Time to work. At least half of the dialogue of the video was spent naming direct labor employees and their supervisors, recognizing their accomplishments in setting up the system.

Bently Nevada was no different. Posters proudly showed division groups of workers touting their successes. But displays and charts are not enough. At Bently Nevada, Bacon is out on the floor walking the plant daily, hourly. In fact, if you phone him, you'll rarely find him at his desk. He knows 95 percent of their 400 plus employees by first name. When a directive or a request for input goes out, Bacon issues a handwritten note. There are no doors to his office, which is covered with little signs. One says "Do What's Right," which he borrowed from Steelcase. Another says, "Create a Causal Atmosphere."

What is a causal atmosphere? It is one where everybody causes things to happen. Bacon doesn't want problems hidden. He wants his people to dig in and uncover what's gumming up the works. He wants them to *do what's right*. He wants them to be thinking. It's little wonder that the employees at Bently Nevada are loyal. As Bacon says, "If you feel you are part of the solution, that you have control over your destiny, you're going to stay. If you're being treated like cattle or a commodity, you're not."

In the early 60's, Douglas McGregor wrote a book called *The Human Side of Enterprise*. This book brought forth the notion known as "Theory Y." McGregor's theory was that people did not hate to work. They actually needed it to satisfy their human needs. His second point was that people give their best efforts when they are committed to an objective. No one found fault with McGregor on these two points, but his final contention drew all kinds of derisive comments. It stated that the population could be convinced to make the company's objectives their own.

No one believed that could happen, but Just-in-Time, together with the cultural changes necessary to make it run, seems to be doing just that. As Omark's Donigan says, "everybody wants to do a good job." They want to feel a part of the operation. They are willing to make the company's objectives their own when they feel their participation is valued and can make a difference in the end result.

But a Just-in-Time company can't make the mistake of measuring a worker solely on output. Hewlett-Packard has virtually eliminated that as an employee evaluation point. To them it is far more important that their workers are good team players, their quality is good, they meet their schedules, they have the skills, there is process improvement, and they are flexible and cross-trained. Pushing output is often at the price of poor quality. But when you tell an employee that if you find a problem you stop the line, it says "we want output, but more importantly, we want our product made right." As we will discuss in Chapter 13, this demands that the right measurements be in place. Without them problems could arise. Nonetheless, that kind of dedication to the product produced immediately instills a sense of company pride, which travels through to every employee.

No Layoff

One of the problems faced by management in establishing a Just-in-Time environment is if the route traveled is to eliminate waste and to improve productivity, what happens when improved productivity eliminates a job? Some companies have met this problem by establishing "no-layoff" policies. Due to the volatility of some businesses, this often can't be a reasonable labor benefit. But common to the companies to which we spoke was the belief that employees would not be laid off because of productivity improvements.

The reality of the manufacturing business says that there will be times when this is unavoidable. A company can explain this to workers by communicating the fall in market demand over and above productivity increases. Though lay-offs may be necessary there are many ways to handle them; attrition, early retirements, and retraining are a few.

When these instances arise at the Tennant Company, the company tries to offer the workers retraining and placement elsewhere in the facility. As Duane Davis explained, "We try to protect people's jobs, offering them opportunities to do something new." The same was true at all the plants contacted. It would seem only right if you're going to ask employees to come up with ideas that are going to improve productivity, and which could eliminate their jobs, that they feel assured the company will recognize that and provide for them. If not, when the company asks for a second round of help, there aren't going to be a lot of volunteers.

Those companies implementing Just-in-Time, who are actively communicating with their employees, seem to be moving in the direction of eliminating layoffs whenever possible. Hire-and-fire companies usually have very poor morale.

Making Mistakes

When an employee knows his company is encouraging him to think, and he offers a suggestion which is implemented but turns out not to work, how that company deals with him will say a lot to the rest of the employees. If he is summarily handed his pink slip, word will quickly spread that the company won't accept failure, and the number of workers then willing to risk their job to improve production will plummet. This does not mean the failed attempt is to be lauded but rather learned from and considered part of the process. As Thomas Edison would say, "Another thing we know is not the answer."

Bently Nevada's Bacon recounts the story about the IBM executive who had made a mistake that had cost the company several million dollars. Expecting to be fired when called in to account for this, he was surprised to find that was not the case. In fact, he was told that the company couldn't afford to fire him. They had just spent several million dollars teaching him a very important lesson.

People make mistakes, and though this should never be accepted as an excuse, firing someone for one is not always the most productive way of dealing with the problem. Mistakes can be a vital sign to a company that people are attempting new things. It has been said, "If people never stumble, it is probably because they are standing still." If mistakes are handled properly, it makes people realize they have to go back and reexamine the process. This can only lead to making better decisions in the future.

But just because a company doesn't fire an employee doesn't mean that everything is necessarily all right with the way they handle mistakes. Some companies in trying to set an example often turn to embarrassing the person who errs, purposefully making him look foolish in the eyes of his co-workers. This has the same effect as firing someone for making a mistake: people will then do only what is safe. In this atmosphere people are afraid to change, so the concept of innovating new ideas is virtually impossible.

SUMMARY

The key to acknowledging the thinking worker is receptivity. It's making a better quality of life for everyone from the top boss to the floor sweeper. That means first treating everyone in the atmosphere as adults, then offering direction, opportunity, and recognition. As these companies have demonstrated, when a worker is properly encouraged to think, to participate, to become multifaceted, everyone wins. The thinking worker is the ingredient that makes Just-in-Time not only successful, but possible.

In the last two chapters we have focused on the involvement of people in the Just-in-Time approach. The next chapter will move directly onto the shop floor, applying these concepts to the notion of lowering order quantities and the benefits that arise from building this first bridge between the people and the plant. Though we may discuss these various ingredients separately, it is important to keep in mind that they work in Just-in-Time not as individual units but as integrated cogs. Each ingredient can stand alone, but by meshing with the other elements a structure with great strength can be built.

Chapter 5

Shrinking Order Quantities

"WE REMOVED ALL ALLOWANCES FOR SETUPS. EACH DEPARTMENT GETS HIT WITH SETUPS AS A VARIANCE."

Traditionally, we have believed that large order quantities are needed to keep costs down. By producing large quantities high setup costs could be amortized over a greater number of items. This idea was supported by the economic order quantity, whose formula established the optimum size for each particular order quantity based on its annual requirements and costs.

But even when a company determined what the economic order quantity was, it usually followed a simpler rule of thumb: Big is better. In many cases this was with valid justification, since it was believed that there was nothing that really could be done to reduce setup times. There was also no pressing reason to do so.

With the arrival of Just-in-Time, though, people began to raise questions about ways to reduce the high costs of manufacturing. The most significant way was to reduce inventory. Immediately, there was a pressing need to figure out how to reduce large order quantities.

But there were still a number of obstacles in the way. The most difficult of these problems was the one associated with changing attitudes toward large order quantities in the first place. Then there were long and expensive setup times, quantity price breaks, and inspection, transportation, and freight costs. There were also the issues of increased paperwork and the impact smaller order quantities have on the stockroom. Just-in-Time companies have met this challenge by first attacking the two greatest barriers to lower order quantities: attitudes and setups.

63

CHANGING ATTITUDES

In most companies, the odds are probably in favor of the shop clearly voicing their complaints about order quantities being too small. Rarely would you hear a complaint about them being too large. Omark tells a story about a punch press they used to run, which they proudly pointed to and said, "We never pulled that thing for less than 3,000,000 strokes."

To assure peace on the floor, planners often err on the side of making quantities too large. When the big push comes for cost reduction and improving efficiency, larger order quantities seem justified. The planners also know the practice will be supported by the vice president of manufacturing and the plant manager. In many companies the principle is, "Always make at least a three-month supply." This often overrides even the economic order quantity for that component.

The question Just-in-Time asks again is, "Why?" Challenging traditional attitudes can, in and of itself, bring about change. Many times order quantities can be reduced by edict—simply scheduling less when a work order is released. But there is a caution to taking this approach: Change reality first, before you change the planning and scheduling system. The rate for inventory reduction must equal the speed at which the problems can be solved. By following this advice the possibility of encountering major obstacles can be lessened.

However, a company should not pass up the opportunity to reduce added fat that has been put on in layers over the years. Reality may not require change in these cases. High order quantities may be the result of poor practices in planning and scheduling alone. So if the prevailing attitude at a company has been "bigger is better," chances are good that reducing order quantities won't expose any rocks that will bring the boat down before they can be removed. Nonetheless, when reducing the order quantity it is essential to do so with your eyes open.

REDUCING SETUP TIMES

The greatest variable in the economic order quantity equation is setup cost. The ideal situation would be zero setup times and zero setup costs to make an order quantity of one. Though this may not be realistic for all parts, it is the direction in which Just-in-Time is moving. The point is, as setup costs approach zero you can afford to make only one—or you can make three or you can make 1000. You make what you need, but never more than that.

One starts attacking long setups by first recognizing that setup reduction is an essential move to lower order quantities, shorten lead times, and reduce inventory. This can be done in quality circle or team meetings, where the advantages of setup time reductions can be charted against some of the disadvantages of economic order quantities. (See Figure 5-1.)

Once these points have been made, what may prove to be the best way to engage the work force in this pursuit is to present the reduction of setup times as a challenge. This is not a false attempt at motivation. Reducing setup times *is* a challenge, but the rewards of meeting the challenge will streamline the flow and improve the process.

Setups have been defined as "the time from making the last good part (prior part number) to the next good one (new part number). Traditionally, these periods can range in time from days to a couple of seconds. Many large machines have setup times in the four- to eight-hour range. One company we spoke with told of a large press that had a setup time of eight hours. They furiously went to work on reducing

---

Large Order Quantity Disadvantages

1. Larger WIP inventories
2. The need for extra storage space and increased storage costs
3. Lower quality
4. A greater chance for obsolescence
5. Increased material handling costs
6. Difficult to level work on the shop floor

Advantages of Reduced Order Quantity

1. Reduced inventory
2. Improved product quality
3. Reduced space requirements
4. Increased capacity—if total setup times are reduced
5. Better use of equipment and labor

Figure 5-1. Advantages and Disadvantages of Order Quantities

it, and brought the time down to four hours. Upon going to their sister plant in Japan, they saw the same machine set up in eleven minutes. They realized they still had a way to go.

Reducing setup time has been compared to a pit crew at the Indianapolis 500. While it may take most people fifteen to twenty minutes to change a tire, and another five minutes to fill a gas tank, pit crews do all of those same things in less than 15 seconds. They do it by closely examining the process, using the right tools, eliminating any wasted moves, having lots of practice, and having a strong incentive to be faster.

Setup reductions don't happen overnight. The first step is to look at the very simple, commonsense things. Lowering setup times does not normally require spending great sums of money. Most advantages come by just paying attention to what is being done, and doing it better. This means enlisting the operators involved with the setup and running of the machine. The companies we spoke with confirmed that most of the suggestions they received were related to improving existing methods rather than major capital expenditures for new equipment.

CONCEPTS AND TECHNIQUES FOR REDUCING SETUPS

In the 1950's Shigeo Shingo, currently the president of the Institute of Management Improvement, began work on a setup reduction process which would later be called *SMED*—Single Minute Exchange of Die. Single minute in this case referred to reducing setup times below ten minutes. To accomplish these ends Shingo first divided the physical setup process into two segments:

Internal setups. Those activities that can only be conducted when the machine is stopped, such as mounting and removing dies. These are items which will interrupt the run time.
External setups. Those activities that can take place while the machine is running, such as transporting dies between storage and machine. These are items external to the run time, which don't interrupt it.

These activities were further defined into conceptual stages:

1. Separate the internal setup from the external setup.
2. Convert, where possible, the internal setup to the external setup.
3. Eliminate the adjustment process.
4. Eventually, abolish the setup itself.

One of the keys to SMED is performing setup activities in a parallel sequence, as opposed to a serial mode. In other words, many of the elements necessary to reduce setups can be accomplished at the same time, rather than waiting for an operational step to be completed before the next step is taken.

The initial driver for all Just-in-Time operations is to involve the workers—form a team to examine the problem and then have them make suggestions. Some of the people who should be on the setup team are the setup operators, a person from quality control, a couple of machine operators, and tool and die engineers.

An excellent first step is to videotape the complete setup operation that is to be reduced. Upon viewing the video some rather strange things will probably appear that weren't apparent before the taping. Operators should begin asking, "Why did I do that?" Or "Look where I had to go to get that wrench." Videotaping the process makes the problems and wasted moves obvious. A company should continue to tape and examine the footage as they step through the process of getting all the bugs out, reviewing each step to see where it could be improved.

After viewing the tape the toolmakers can get together with the operators to make any necessary changes. In attacking their setups, Steelcase worked under the assumption that as long as what the operators wanted was within reason, give it to them. With Shingo's concepts guiding the way, the process can begin in earnest.

Adjustable gauges can be replaced with permanent preset ones, which work particularly well in a high-volume business. Often, tooling can be preset and bolt sizes standardized.

Steelcase saw on their video that their people had to walk around the large presses to connect different hoses, rather than attaching them all from one place. The solution was to put all hoses and electric probes on one side of the die. Then they color coded the hose connections, and where any connection might be a problem, they put left threads versus right threads.

Setup operators have also found that it's often best to use die carriers, rolling tables the same height as the press bed, which will eliminate the need to track down a forklift operator. Another idea is to place locating pins in the dies, which can speed up the process enormously while improving the accuracy of getting the die in the right place the first time.

Another aspect Steelcase discovered was that when a forklift driver came to get the old die, he arrived empty, and when he brought back the new die, he left empty, thus making two unnecessary trips. He now brings the new die and returns with the old. Steelcase also equipped their drivers with two-way radios, so they could be alerted in advance as to when a die change was about to be made.

In order to make sure all the parts arrive at the right time to make a changeover, the tool crib attendant should have a setup check-off list with all the auxiliary pieces and equipment needed and arranged prior to the setup. By doing this the operator no longer has to run all over the place to get what he needs. Everybody knows where everything is supposed to be, and that's where it will be found.

Being able to find an unseen part left in a die has prompted some companies to add tonnage monitors to their press breaks. This will help prevent the ruin of the die, which cannot be visually seen otherwise. Finally, the completed setup should be photographed, so that on subsequent changeovers the setup man can make sure he has it right and ready for the operator.

By reducing setups and then being able to schedule parts to be produced more frequently, a highly repetitive manufacturing company will find an improvement in the quality of components. Short setups offer a quick feedback loop to let operators know within three or four hours if their part quality was good.

When all is said and done, what a company will find is that the majority of setup reduction techniques are not much more than using common sense. (See Figure 5-2.)

One point that needs to be recognized is that the total direct labor dedicated to setups may not change. This is because of the parallel procedures of off-line setup preparations and the use of more frequent setups. Though reducing setup times may not reduce the total setup costs, the benefits derived from these procedures will drive down overall costs by reducing inventories via reduced order quantities, and improve quality by reducing the feedback loop. (See Figure 5-3.)

Another fallout of accurate and reliable setups at Steelcase, due primarily to preset gauging, was that it lowered the number of reworked parts. In many cases, they were able to come away with the first hit on the press being a good part. When measuring setup times from the last good part of the old component to the first good part of the new, that's exactly the result you want. This ability dramatically lowered their scrap rate, too.

Having accepted setup times as a given, most companies have never

1. Standardize the external setup actions; replace adjustable gauges with permanent ones.
2. Put all probe and blow-off hoses on one side of die.
3. Put a bench at side of press at the same level as the press opening, to hold the next die.
4. Color code all hose connections: air, hydraulic, water, etc.
5. Use parallel operations—Deliver all components to support setup die (Use a check-off sheet to insure all are present prior to setup).
6. Design a quick locating system—positioning pins and holes, with quick fasteners.
7. Standardize all die receptacles.
8. Add tonnage monitor on press to detect two pieces in die before damaging dies.
9. Involve tool and die designers in setup reduction programs so all new designs incorporate quick changeover concepts.
10. Use two-way radio between setup man and lift truck operator who removes and delivers dies.
11. Photograph completed operation as a guide for setup man: Location of tables, wrenches, baskets, etc.
12. Review material flow charts with reduced movements in mind.
13. Make as many of the setup activities internal to the run time. That is, do as much of the setup as possible without shutting down the machine.
14. Standardize all bolt sizes.
15. Use left- and right-hand thread on bolts that can be interchanged with disastrous results.
16. Code parts on dispatch list for major or minor setups to aid scheduling.
17. Standardization and use of common parts in the product will reduce the number of different parts required. If design engineering does not design a new part, no setup is required for it.

Figure 5-2. Techniques for Reducing Setup Times

really applied their manufacturing engineering standards to the issue. Bently Nevada's Ray Bacon stressed that it was extremely important to educate manufacturing engineering and get them talking to the operators. Then the engineers are able to go back and make the changes necessary to reduce setup times on the shop floor.

Bacon even wrote a productivity standard for the engineering department. The outcome of these efforts has been to standardize Bently Nevada's panel sizes and CAD data bases to make printed circuit boards.

	Frequency	Total
Setup Time	of	Setup
per Changeover $+$	Setups $=$	Time
Decrease	Increase	Down Slightly
($\downarrow$)	($\uparrow$)	($\downarrow$)

Figure 5-3. Total Setup Time

Now, instead of different panels and different instructions for each of their 400 different boards, they're trying to reduce it to only one standard panel size, common drill sizes, and few instruction changes.

If any time spent on setups is a waste, one way to handle this problem may be to make setups a variance. Suddenly, people are accountable for this time waste. Black and Decker tried this approach with a great deal of success. "We removed all allowances for setups," said Black and Decker's Ed Parrish. "Each department now gets hit with setup as a variance." As one might imagine, this motivated Black and Decker department managers to reduce their setups as much as possible, instead of to some predetermined time.

This was one area that Black and Decker did put some money into improving their system. In their injection molding section, they purchased two machines that had automatic mold changing. The machines can be programmed to run as many as five different molds without a mechanic having to physically change the mold.

The rest of Black and Decker's molding machines are all changed over by manpower. That process used to take two people two and a half hours. Through training, and videotaping, they have lowered that time by nearly 50 percent.

Black and Decker's setup people are specially trained and recruited from within the shop. To join this corps, a worker has to go through a training program as a material handler, a stock handler, and a machine operator. Then he must go through another four-week training period with an engineer. After all of that, he is then judged by his peers. If the other workers don't think he is going to make it, he doesn't get the job. When setups are considered a variance, Black and Decker wants to make sure they've got the right person on the job.

One way Steelcase has made sure that the right people in some of their subsidiary divisions perform their setups properly is also through videotape. When a particularly complicated setup has reached a high degree of proficiency, they will videotape the complete process, using the setup and machine operators normally involved as their actors. These tapes are then shipped out to Steelcase's various subsidiaries to act as teaching aids. As Joe Lauria suggested, if one picture is worth a thousand words, a videotape is worth a million.

PAPERWORK

Another obstacle to lowering order quantities is the increase in paperwork that occurs. Smaller quantities produced more frequently can quickly amass a mountain of work orders, order releases, and stockroom pick lists.

Could the process work if there were no work orders? Often, the answer is yes. Typically, work orders require a great amount of care and feeding. They have to be created. They often have to be rescheduled. They have to be received and closed out. Companies began examining this process and appropriately asked, "How can we simplify work orders?" The reason they were created in the first place was to keep track of the flow from one operation to the next. This becomes essential for large order quantities with long cycle times. But with smaller order quantities, product moves through the line much faster, and the need for accurate tracking is greatly lessened, as is the need for work orders.

We will examine how this elimination of work orders impacts the scheduling of component requirements in Chapter 7. For now, it is important to note that this obstacle can effectively be addressed, simplifying the process as it goes.

Companies have used the post-deduct process to overcome the problems that are thrust on their stockrooms when they begin manufacturing smaller order quantities. Whenever throughput times have been shortened, and tracking is not as critical, the material used can be deducted after the product has been built, eliminating a lot of transactions. This technique is also referred to as "backflushing." There are some problems associated with this approach, which are outlined in Chapter 12. But if product cycle times are short enough, or intermediate deduct points throughout the process are used, and inventory reconciliation is handled properly, post-deduct has shown itself to be a good candidate to help relieve some of the paperwork.

QUANTITY PRICE BREAKS

Discounts for larger quantity orders have been offered as a standard approach to lowering costs. This is another reason why suppliers need to be brought into the process early. By helping them address the necessary attitude change about producing smaller order quantities, by showing them steps to reduce setup times and costs, by demonstrating tested ways of making their operations more efficient, by offering them visibility into future needs—the issue of price breaks for quantity can be all but eliminated by the cost savings realized by the supplier.

TRANSPORTATION

Another difficulty and expense with receiving daily deliveries of smaller order quantities are the transportation costs. Though this will be discussed in greater detail in Chapter 10, there are ways to reduce this problem by making it more efficient. The Tennant Company, Hewlett-Packard, and Xerox have all instituted "milk run" programs, having trucks pick up on a daily route from a number of suppliers in their general vicinity. Another answer is freight consolidation. Again, though problems may exist, people are finding solutions to satisfy their needs.

IMPACT ON THE STOCKROOM

Handling the material needs of smaller and more frequently produced parts and orders could wreak havoc on an unprepared stockroom. Putting together the increased kits, moving material and keeping track of the multiplying transactions could effectively handcuff stores personnel, causing delays and line shutdowns.

The answer to this problem at some companies has been either to redesign their stockroom to accommodate Just-in-Time deliveries and shipments or to institute a system like Hewlett-Packard's, which is fairly close to a dock to work-in-process notion. In this way materials come in, and within a few hours they are sent to point-of-use storage areas. The impact on the stockroom is lessened while productivity is improved.

POINT-OF-USE STORAGE

Shifting the load off the stockroom is exactly what point-of-use storage is all about. As the name implies, this places inventory at the actual point of use. Point-of-use storage means a company can once again avoid double handling of material, reducing the possibility of damage.

To make this technique work, it is important that the quantity at the point of use is small; otherwise a company is doing nothing more than relocating the stockroom. Without the element of rapid turnover, the associated problems of accuracy and stationary inventory will invariably crop up. Even with the proper flow, an important consideration for any company is that point-of-use storage is as dependent on the integrity of inventory record accuracy as material stored in the stockroom.

INSPECTION COSTS

As will be detailed in the chapter to follow, inspection is another area affected by the reduction of order quantities. This, again, is good news. With order quantities reduced, quality issues take on even greater significance. Because there is less material traveling down the line, quality problems can be spotted quickly, especially when the responsibility for inspection is turned over to the operator at the source. As order quantities approach one, quality problems need to be detected before they are passed on to the next work station, or the line could be shut down. By transferring inspection duties to the source, many of the internal inspection and testing steps can be eliminated. As has been said, "Inspectors do nothing to improve quality, they only monitor a process after it's too late." After initiating their Just-in-Time program, Tektronix was able to reduce their incoming inspection staff from 100 down to one.

SUMMARY

One of the keys to reducing work-in-process inventories is to attack the traditional roadblocks to lower order quantities. This means changing both the visible and invisible issues of manufacturing; changing attitudes is an invisible process and therefore is one step that is often overlooked. Reducing setup times, addressing the impact on stock-rooms, transportation, suppliers, and inspection are the visible issues. By taking both the seen and unseen steps, significant reductions can also be realized in lead times, floor space, scrap, and rework, while adding substantially to the quality of the product. Reducing order quantities has been a vital and powerful contributor to the success of many Just-in-Time programs, offering substantial savings throughout the manufacturing environment.

In the chapter to follow, we will examine another of the primary ingredients of Just-in-Time, the need for excellent quality.

Chapter 6

Taking the Quality High Road

"WHAT CAN BE MORE WASTEFUL THAN NOT MAKING SOMETHING RIGHT THE FIRST TIME?"

When Phil Crosby said, "Quality is free," what he meant was that the cost of poor quality can be tremendous. Specifically, he listed such added costs as product redesign, rework, scrap, reservicing delivered products, and lost customer credibility. In a Just-in-Time environment all of these costs are seen as waste. But it is important to note that quality is far more than simply a component of Just-in-Time. It is a critical issue in and of itself, and one that must be addressed by every manufacturing company over and above Just-in-Time.

Before we journey too far into the issues surrounding quality, we should also mention that it would be virtually impossible to address the complete topic of quality in one chapter. Many authorities have spent whole books outlining and diagraming their various approaches to the subject. What we can do is try to examine some of these different approaches and how they relate to Just-in-Time.

Crosby has defined quality as "conformance to requirements." That is, does the part/product do what it is supposed to do? If it doesn't, there's a quality problem. What he proposed as a high bar to motivate excellent quality was the notion of "Zero Defects." Though this is considered to be a statistical impossibility, by working toward zero defects it means quality can free itself of the added costs that arise when parts do not conform to their requirements.

"What can be more wasteful," asks Xerox's Pierre Landry, "than not making something right the first time?" Poor quality is not a new problem for many companies, but it certainly is an expensive one. For every quality problem that rears its head, there is a corresponding neg-

75

ative reaction that resounds throughout the manufacturing process, affecting customer relations, schedules, and productivity.

Two other American pioneers who have had a major impact in the field of quality are J.M. Juran and W. Edward Deming. Juran looked at quality in a somewhat different fashion than Crosby. For Juran quality was defined as a product's "fitness for use." Does the product produced meet the requirements of the user? Both Deming and Juran placed a great deal of emphasis on the statistical aspects of quality, the "measurable standards of quality," which we will discuss later.

Deming has often been considered the father of Japanese quality programs, having made repeated trips to Japan over the past thirty years. There is in fact a Deming Prize awarded in Japan to the manufacturer that has demonstrated the finest quality performance. The point of this is while the principles of quality control may have originated in America, the Japanese embraced them. They have set the high bar of opportunity. Now it is up to American manufacturing to meet it. The objective is to measure quality defects in parts per million, as opposed to accepting a quality standard of 98 percent.

The importance of good quality in a Just-in-Time environment is also directly tied to the level of inventory. As inventory levels are reduced, buffer stocks eliminated, and line flow balanced, quality must excel or it will mean shutting down the line when problems surface.

We spoke earlier about the inventory analogy of lowering the water to expose the rocks. There are, of course, some quality obstacles evident before the water level is even touched, and they should be eliminated before anything else is done. A good quality program *requires* fixing any and all problems as soon as they are discovered. But as to the problems that lie submerged beneath the surface, there are a couple of approaches for dealing with them.

The first approach is to lower the water, dealing with the problems as they surface. The second, rather than waiting, is to use a little sonar, or even send down a diver to assess what kind of problems exist. Though most companies have a good idea what their problems are, a little caution can prevent a big surprise. As with the implementation of other Just-in-Time elements, starting small is advisable. It is not always necessary to make a crisis out of problems in order to fix them. This is true in spite of the fact that some companies don't react until they feel a high level of pain. Just-in-Time is about eliminating pain in the manufacturing process, but that doesn't mean a company *has* to feel greater pain before they act. There's no need to make things worse!

As discussed in the previous chapter on order quantities, one way to begin eliminating obstacles is a return to the process of *quality at the source*. Quality at the source is a return to the notion of personal accountability for quality. When manufacturing evolved to a division of labor, there was no longer one person accountable for quality. Inspectors became necessary to assure quality standards were being maintained. In essence, by taking quality away from the person doing the work, we were trying to inspect quality into the product after it was produced. Scrap was inevitable. That does not have to be the case. The point is that it is easier and less costly to build quality into the product than to try to correct the problem later.

Companies have found that by returning the responsibility and accountability for quality back to the operator, they have eliminated the need for this separate and costly inspection.

What is being seen, contrary to what many have thought, is at a certain point quality actually lowers cost while it improves productivity. The conventional wisdom has always said, ''As quality increases, costs increase.'' The Japanese found that quality does not have to cost more (see Figure 6-1). In the beginning the price of quality tends to rise as these measures are implemented. But as quality increases, costs eventually start to go down. Because of the shape of this graphed curve, the Japanese call this the Mt. Fuji effect.

This is easy to understand when one examines the definition of pro-

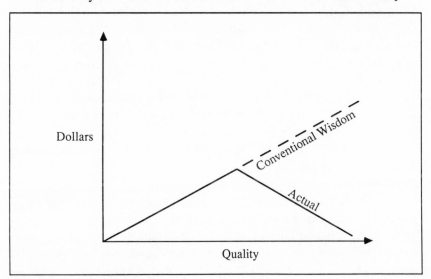

Figure 6-1. Mt. Fuji Effect

ductivity—output divided by input. Poor quality in this equation equals less output with the same input.

In order to attack quality problems, it is important to be able to identify their source. The Japanese believe that quality problems are a 30/30/40 proposition. That is, 30 percent are caused by manufacturing, 30 percent caused by vendors, and, surprisingly, 40 percent are caused by engineering.

With this as a starting point, we can now delve into some of the problems and solutions a company must address in these three areas to improve its quality while preparing itself for Just-In- Time.

TOTAL QUALITY CONTROL

The traditional approach to quality control in manufacturing has been to make a batch of say 1000 parts on a machine, and then take a statistically valid sample of the lot, the objective being to provide a series of planned measurements to verify that acceptable products were produced. The sampling would reveal the percentage of rejects found in the lot. This percentage could then be held up against the allowable number of rejects to determine whether the quality level was acceptable or not. In essence, whether it was a good or bad lot of parts.

During the last thirty years or so, another approach to quality was developed. Calling on the work of A.V. Feigenbaum and his book *Total Quality Control*, with refinements brought about by W. Edwards Deming and others, Total Quality Control (TQC) came into being. The overriding focus of TQC is to make the product right the first time. This means maintaining the process so it doesn't go out of control, and assigning responsibility and accountability to the person doing the work by allowing the workers to stop the process when it starts to deviate. Feigenbaum was calling for this in the early 1960s, but it was not until the Japanese picked up on Deming's polishing of the concept that American manufacturing began recognizing the impact of Total Quality Control.

Deming said that rather than waiting until the part/product had been produced, measure the process while it was being made and stop it before it went out of control. In a Just-in-Time environment, with reduced order quantities and little or no safety stock, this is particularly critical. The technique for accomplishing this is known as *Statistical Process Control* (SPC). (See Figure 6-2.)

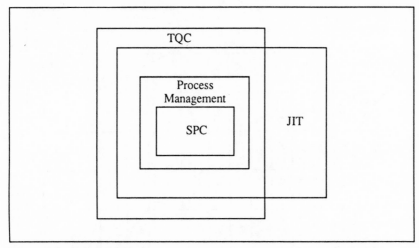

Figure 6-2. Interface Chart

STATISTICAL PROCESS CONTROL

Statistical Process Control simply provides measurements to monitor the process in order to get and keep it under control. These monitors could be either a piece of equipment or a flip chart with handwritten notes. The key aspect is that the process is constantly being watched. This allows a company to produce at a very high quality level while identifying immediately a process that's going to make bad pieces. Simultaneously, it eliminates the need for separate inspection steps.

One example of SPC is the use of a quality control process chart, which the machine generates as it runs the parts. The chart measures the vital parameters established for each item, determining the conformance of each to the desired result. Jack Warne, former president of Omark Industries, refers to this as "the process talking to you, and all you have to do is listen." This enables the operators to stop the process before it goes out of control. Then the problems can be corrected. The key point to this process really working is to make sure the correction is not merely a superficial quick fix, but that the corrective action goes to the root of the problem. Once the flow has been improved, keeping the process in control becomes even easier. (See Figure 6-3 and Figure 6-4.) Some interpretation is required when using statistical control charts. Figure 6-4 indicates the process is in control until 8:00. However, because seven or more points are recorded between the centerline and the 3 sigma upper control limit, it

Product: Gear Case   Operation: Pressing Bearing in Gear Case
Machine: Machine #1   Control Limits: .2505—.2513

Time	10:00	12:30	3:00	5:00	6:40	9:20	8:00	10:00	12:30	3:00	4:30	7:00	10:00
Measurements	2519	2510	2503	2515	2513	2510	2520	2510	2510	2507	2501	2502	2518
	2519	2510	2503	2515	2512	2509	2521	2509	2516	2507	2501	2501	2518
	2519	2510	2502	2515	2511	2504	2522	2508	2510	2504	2501	2502	2515
	2515	2513	2507	2515	2511	2504	2521	2507	2516	2500	2501	2502	2516
	2515	2509	2505	2513	2510	2504	2518	2507	2516	2500	2502	2509	2517
Total	12587	12552	12520	12573	12557	12531	12602	12541	12568	12518	12506	12516	12584
Average	2517	2510	2504	2515	2511	2506	2521	2508	2514	2503	2501	2503	2517

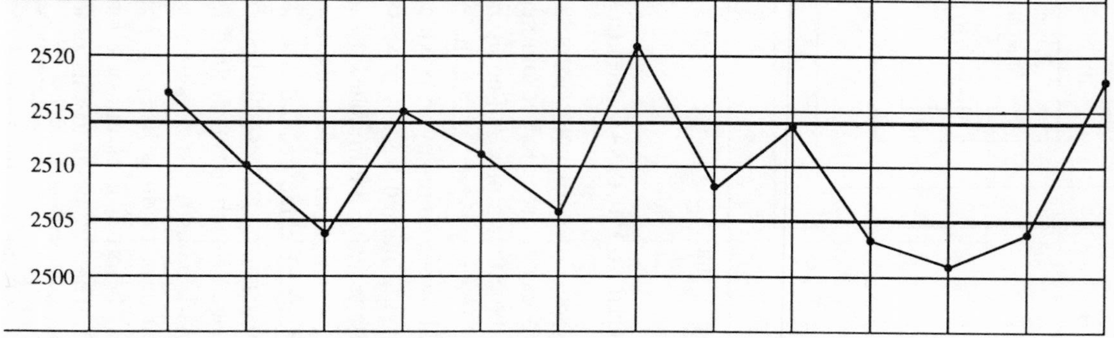

2520
2515
2510
2505
2500

Figure 6-3.   Statistical Process Control Chart—Out of Control

Product: Gear Case
Machine: Machine #1

Operation: Pressing Bearing in Gear Case
Control Limits: .2505–.2513

Time	7:00	12:30	3:00	6:30	9:00	7:00	10:00	12:30	3:00	5:30	6:30	8:00	9:15
Measurements	2510	2511	2510	2509	2512	2513	2511	2512	2513	2514	2509	2513	2512
	2510	2510	2510	2509	2512	2513	2514	2512	2510	2513	2510	2513	2513
	2510	2511	2510	2509	2512	2513	2514	2512	2510	2510	2512	2514	2514
	2510	2511	2510	2510	2511	2513	2513	2513	2510	2512	2512	2514	2513
	2510	2511	2510	2510	2512	2513	2513	2510	2510	2510	2509	2513	2514
Total	12550	12554	12550	12547	12559	12565	12565	12559	12553	12559	12552	12567	12566
Average	2510	2511	2510	2509	2512	2513	2513	2512	2511	2512	2510	2513	2513

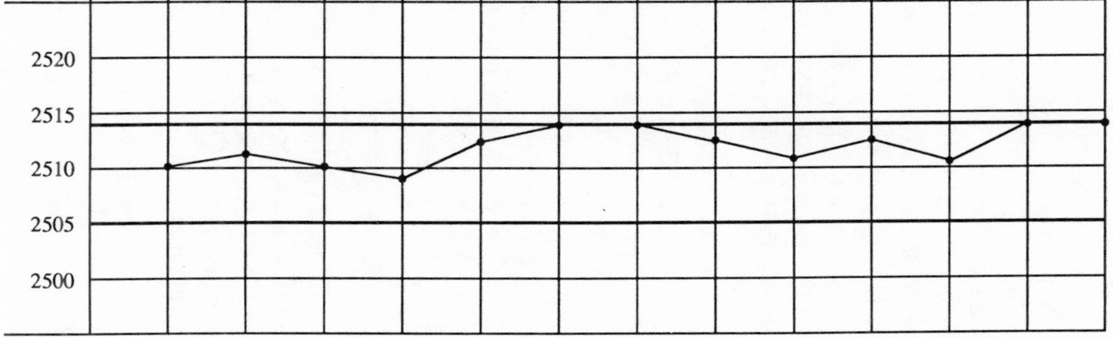

2520

2515

2510

2505

2500

Figure 6-4. Statistical Process Control Chart—In Control

is as much an indication that the process is out of control as when a single point exceeds the control limit.

Vern Pearson at Omark didn't realize until after the fact that "the best way to sell inventory reductions was to preach quality gains." Using the principles of Total Quality Control to establish good process control, he discovered "the closer you are to the area a problem is found, the quicker you will find a solution."

Pearson is describing the short feedback loop necessary to determine quality problems. Just-in-Time won't allow problems to travel down the line for someone else to catch, because the next operation in line is dependent on receiving a good part. The short feedback loop also lets an operator who has received a bad part know exactly where it came from and who was responsible for making it. Quality has to come from the source.

One of Omark's techniques for improving quality was to establish a Quality Information Center (QIC), with quality bulletin boards holding examples of parts with chronic defects. By working with a team made up of people from marketing, design engineering, manufacturing engineering, a supervisor and an operator, the center will set a specification target along with a QIC sample. That sample is the operator's guide. Then as the quality improves, they are able to tighten those tolerances. As Omark's Pearson reiterates, "Quality is constant improvement."

STOPPING THE LINE

The idea of stopping the line in the middle of production to fix a quality problem is an alien concept to some manufacturing concerns. It's just not done! Well, let's say it wasn't done.

Hewlett-Packard's Charlene Adair says, "The worst things that can happen (in order of priority) in a manufacturing process are":

1. To produce bad product.
2. To hide problems and inefficiencies with inventory.
3. To interrupt the flow of product.

In the early days of Hewlett-Packard's Just-in-Time implementation, no sooner had they gotten the system running than an operator shut down the line because of a quality problem. Needless to say, this made the production manager very nervous. On the very first day of getting Just-in-Time rolling, production wasn't improving; it wasn't even producing! The second day was much like the first, and the manager couldn't take it. Finally, he just left the plant during the line stops, so he at least didn't have to watch his plant grind to a halt.

In spite of this rocky beginning, they soon ironed out the bugs, and by month's end had met their production goals. In fact, in most cases, H-P experienced increased output, even though the line was being sporadically shut down for problems.

When you stop the line it focuses everything on the immediate resolution of the problem. It doesn't allow for sweeping the problem under the table.

These quality issues are as true for repetitive manufacturers as they are for those whose process is more intermittent, producing one special item after another. The Tennant Company was a low-volume repetitive manufacturer that was quite surprised by the quality problems they unearthed when they lowered their inventory. They were running non-finished goods inventory levels of about $23,000,000 before their Just-in-Time efforts. They lowered that level by about 20 percent to $17,000,000. Suddenly, quality problems appeared that had been hidden by the excess inventory, problems that affected product flow. They quickly discovered that a quality defect in the flow affected the entire process. Now, they had to be corrected at the source, where once they were sent down the line for someone else to handle.

Xerox attacked similar problems by instituting a company-wide program of benchmarking—setting the high bar for various operations, as compared to the competition. They began measuring their defect rate in parts per million. (See Figure 6-5.) In 1980 they were producing as many as 10,000 defects per million parts, compared to their Japanese sister company, Fuji Xerox, that was running 1500. Xerox went to work and significantly reduced their figure to 1620. (Fuji Xerox, in the meantime, dropped down to 750.) "The reason we've been able to do this," say Pierre Landry, "is primarily because of statistical process control." They are now aiming for 750.

Omark had recently received a shipment of rivet wire from their vendor, which they put into process. But when the wire came to the assembly operator, she thought the rivets didn't look right. They weren't spinning the right way. She stopped the process immediately. The suspect parts were sent to Omark's metallurgist, who found there was indeed something wrong. The vendor had inadvertently mixed the wrong kind of wire into the raw material. They had received a truckload of the wire, but because of the quality system they had in place, and the emphasis on employee responsibility, there were only four pans of

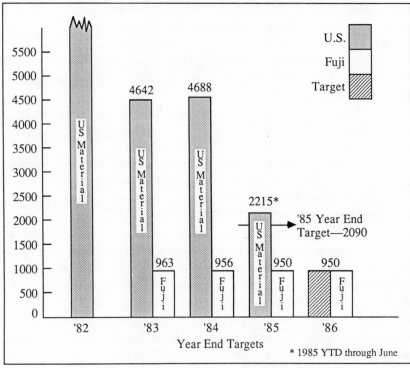

Figure 6-5. Xerox Bar Chart

material in process that needed to be scrapped.

Black and Decker has instituted another kind of quality control measure to avoid any unintended oversights in the preparation of their products. The technique is called a "pokayoke." This comes from the Japanese word "bakayoke," meaning "foolproof." In Black and Decker's case, one of their greatest customer complaints has been a problem with missing parts or literature. Their pokayoke device will not let a package go until every necessary piece is in the box. An operator flips a switch in front of a series of boxes filled with different warranty cards, instructions, and the like. Each time the operator puts a hand into a box a light goes on, which signals the material has been taken. The box will not advance to the final shipping area until all lights have been lit.

Pokayokes can also take the form of a device to prevent a part from being placed in the wrong spot. For example, by making threads on one component right-handed, while threads on an adjacent component are left-handed, it produces a foolproof operation—a component can only be placed in the proper spot.

Black and Decker has trained all of their operators in Total Quality Control methods, and they are held accountable for what they produce. Their quality results speak for the effectiveness of their efforts. (See Figure 6-6.)

QUALITY CIRCLES

A few years ago, quality circles were the rage. American manufacturing, with its quick-fix mentality, tried to tap the Japanese productivity bank and came up with quality circles. These groups of employees joined together for daily, weekly, or monthly meetings to discuss how to improve not only the company's quality but other problems as well. Quality circles by themselves were mostly talk. Over the long run, companies discovered it was nearly impossible to maintain their enthusiasm and momentum.

There were a couple of reasons for this. Just talking wasn't enough. Many of these sessions saw little action. The tools and environment necessary to act on the suggestions were not in place, and the participants soon tired of management's failed attempt at rallying the troops. Additionally, the employees involved often heard only the company preaching the need for quality, but at month's end it was the same old thing: Get the quality control department to provide a waiver and ship like hell.

The missing element was consistency. By providing mixed messages, and few tools to put their workers' ideas in motion, management reinforced the idea that many of a company's quality problems were not caused by the worker but by management.

Test bench rejects improved 50%

Eliminated in-process inspection by quality department

Reduced quality costs 25%

Using pokayoke technique, have reduced complaints of missing items by 50%

Figure 6-6. Quality Results at Black and Decker

Though quality is a concern that certainly stands alone in importance, Just-in-Time can bring a new atmosphere to bear. An environment can be established that puts a new emphasis on quality, its relationship to lower inventories, and the direct involvement of the workers. At its heart, quality is a management issue, and without that managerial support quality circles are nothing but a lot of talk. Put to their proper use, as a generator of labor ideas coupled with consistent management action, quality circles can be the energy-intensive activity they are supposed to be. Companies like Hewlett-Packard, Steelcase, Xerox, and others have continually demonstrated their effectiveness by supporting the ideas that come out of these daily, weekly, or monthly meetings with consistent action.

VENDORS DELIVERING QUALITY

The concepts of quality have to extend beyond the plant walls to a manufacturer's suppliers as well. If a vendor is shipping out poor quality, those defective parts will stop the Just-in-Time line as quickly as poor parts made by the manufacturer inside the plant.

When Xerox reduced their vendor base from 5000 to 300 the main reason was to improve vendor quality. The 300 were selected in part for their existing quality, but also because they were willing to work with Xerox to become even better. This was not the way things have always been.

Dealing with suppliers in the past meant a certain uneasy trust existed between supplier and customer. Though that trust was often agreed and contracted, what was the normal procedure when a vendor's shipment arrived? It was checked first to make sure the quantity was right. Then it was checked for quality flaws. If the vendor had been doing his own source inspection, both of those repeated inspection steps would have been wasted motions.

The problem was, as everyone knew, "There were few good suppliers." This meant companies had to cover themselves by increasing their sources, and increasing their inventory hedges just in case their suppliers didn't perform (as they often didn't). Xerox was no different. Their vendor quality program was known as receiving inspection. This process, of course, worked no better than it did when they tried to do the same thing with their own parts. You don't inspect quality into your parts.

One objective of Just-in-Time operations is to eliminate incoming inspection. In order for that to work, vendors have to demonstrate they are willing to meet the quality standards of their customer. This implies they must be doing a top notch job of inspection before their product is shipped, or they're doing their own source inspection using statistical process control.

There are three basic steps a company can take to help eliminate receiving inspection:

1. Requirements have to be specified to the supplier so the supplier can understand them.
2. Credibility and trust have to be built between customer and supplier based on performance.
3. Periodic quality audits must be conducted to ensure ongoing compliance.

Once this has been accomplished, the supplier understands what the customer really wants and has a fighting chance to conform to specifications. A company running Just-in-Time with reduced order quantities and no buffer stock will know quickly if a supplier is not living up to their part of the bargain.

Nonetheless, just because a company agrees to improve their quality doesn't necessarily mean they have the means to do it. The Tennant Company brings their vendors into the plant to see how their quality program works and to talk with their quality assurance experts. If their supplier base were still in the thousands, they would have to spend half their manufacturing time educating their vendors.

Xerox, with its reduced vendor base, has also been working closely to help transition their suppliers. They have been able to reduce their incoming inspection group from 225 people to 40, and have doubled their Field Supplier Quality Engineers from 30 to 60. These Supplier Quality Engineers are then sent out on the road to work directly with suppliers that are having problems. They make weekly visits to each vendor, making sure that everybody understands what is happening. They also assure that new vendor employees are being properly trained and that their suppliers' manufacturing processes are under control.

Xerox has made a commitment to SPC, not only in their own plants but in their vendors' as well. They began an education program with all their suppliers when they decided that a company couldn't be a Xerox supplier unless they were doing SPC.

Harley-Davidson demands the same sort of SPC capability from their suppliers as well. They provide classes in SPC to all their vendors, the only cost being the price of a $20 calculator, which each person takes home with them.

Omark is also working on SPC with their vendors. They are involved in an effort to make sure that both their measurements and their vendors' measurements are the same, in terms of specific characteristics. They are refining their process to the point that rather than inspecting anything coming in, the supplier simply sends copies of their SPC charts. Omark can see from the charts that the process is in control and the parts are in compliance.

There has been an unexpected result from this sort of vendor-customer relationship in addition to the reduced lead times, the cost reductions, and the improved quality. As Xerox's Pierre Landry explained, "When Xerox began their SPC education, there was one supplier who said, 'Here comes Xerox with another of those damned ideas that is going to cost me all kinds of money.' But after he got into it," Landry continued, "he found that 'stuff really worked.' He took me into this room and showed me how he established his process controls, certified a part, and where he found the specifications. He then showed me where he stood with all the Xerox parts, as well as the Kodak parts (a competitor of Xerox) that went into their copiers, and the IBM parts, too. The vendor said, 'You know, if it hadn't been for you guys, I wouldn't have it half as good.'"

Being able to overcome this kind of initial reluctance on the part of a supplier, letting them see for themselves how it could benefit them, is one reason why it is important for a company to begin their Just-in-Time operations in house before taking it out to their vendors. It allows them to bring the vendor in, saying, "Here's what we're doing regarding quality in our plant. Take a good look." But even more than that, "We'll be happy to show you how you can do it, too."

By getting vendors to improve their quality, it makes things better not only for the customer but for the vendor, too. As we will see in Chapter 10, when a vendor improves their process, it makes them a better supplier for their other customers as well. This is not a customer win–vendor lose operation. When handled properly, it is definitely win-win. Vendors get their process under control, and customers can reduce their incoming inspection operations, with all the favorable aspects that implies.

PRODUCT DESIGN FOR QUALITY IMPROVEMENT

It has been suggested that the end users are not concerned with how products are made. They are concerned whether or not the products fit their needs, are efficient and reliable, look good, and please them when used. Consequently, making products exactly to specifications and free from defects does not by any means guarantee that the product will satisfy the customer. There are those who believe that the only true test of quality is when the customer is 100 percent satisfied with the product, tells his friends about it, and buys another when he needs it.

Nonetheless, manufacturing still must be concerned with how the product is made. It is critical for design engineers to begin looking not only at the customer but in the other direction, toward the manufacturing floor as well. They need to be designing the product for manufacturability at the zero defect level. As one of Bently Nevada's design engineers, Jack Opocensky, points out, "You can design the most wonderful thing in the world, but if you can't produce it, it's no good."

Bently Nevada builds ultra sensitive transducers which must be able to detect the alignment of powerful turbines. These products have as many as 80,000 different configurations, so the issue of being able to produce them properly is a major concern. It has meant that both manufacturing engineering and design engineering have had to work hand in hand from the conceptual level right on through production to assure manufacturability. As they pointed out, once the product has been designed and tested, a prototype built, and the decision made to manufacture the product, it's an expensive stage to redesign for the quality of manufacturability.

As an example of how this has worked, Bently Nevada has had their design engineering department give up 10 percent of the space on their circuit boards and design in test circuits to speed up the quality testing process. Their testing process used to take 40 hours, but because of engineering's redesign, the same process takes less than *30 minutes*.

In another instance of quality of design, Xerox discovered something which completely surprised them. When they began disassembling copiers made by their sister plant in Japan, Fuji Xerox, the copiers had *more* parts than their American counterparts, not fewer as might be expected. Where a U.S. design might specify one fairly complex part, perhaps injection molded with inserts, the comparable Japanese design would call for a number of smaller and simpler parts. Most of these parts were metal, making them easier to punch out, and because of the principle of compensating tolerances, each piece would not require the same extremely tight limitations. They were, therefore, producing higher quality with fewer rejects and less rework.

A U.S. auto manufacturer has been witnessing a similar situation with the transmissions built in the United States and those built by a Japanese affiliate. The Japanese transmissions have more parts than those designed in Detroit.

As mentioned earlier, the Japanese found that 40 percent of the quality problems that surfaced were caused by faulty design engineering. If the fundamental design of a product is poor, no amount of compensation on the assembly line can help. It becomes imperative that companies begin to see quality as an issue that must be dealt with at every level in the design and manufacturing processes. From the vendor through each and every manufacturing step, operator and engineer, it must be recognized that there is nothing more wasteful than not making something right the first time.

PREVENTIVE MAINTENANCE

One way to assure a product is made right the first time on the shop floor is *preventive maintenance*. If SPC is an essential ingredient of quality for Just-in-Time, then preventive maintenance must be recognized as an absolute necessity for SPC. If preventive maintenance is not faithfully practiced and inventories are reduced, order quantities approach one, and safety stock is eliminated, then one machine out of tolerance could shut down the whole line.

In many cases, American manufacturers have performed maintenance on their machinery only when it's broken or near death. That may make some sense solely in terms of maintenance cost. However, it doesn't make sense when considering the poor quality produced by poorly running machines.

The Japanese, and now many American companies, are saying the notion of "if it's not broken don't fix it" is really begging for trouble. The right answer is prevention, not remedial maintenance. Perform maintenance as a routine exercise; schedule it, plan around it if necessary, but don't let the machine go out of tolerance.

The maintenance department acquires new importance with Just-in-

Time. Since the line stops for down equipment, response from maintenance is critical. No longer are buffers of work-in-process built to work around faulty equipment. This places an added responsibility on preventive maintenance departments to care for the equipment in their charge.

An extension of this idea is that since operators usually understand how their equipment should "feel" better than does anyone else, it is a good idea to let them handle the simple, regular maintenance. At Omark, preventive maintenance took on a whole new meaning when, in the spirit of Just-in-Time, they involved the work force. Engineering and the shop supervisors used to establish the criteria for maintenance. When they involved the operators, who were familiar with the machines, it gave them the advantage of having someone who knew what the particular wear conditions were on the equipment, and what parts should be worked on and replaced.

The essential point is, making quality parts within tolerances and without scrap demands a work force and equipment running at peak performance. Without the use of preventive maintenance techniques, the odds of maintaining a Just-in-Time atmosphere lie somewhere between malfunction and breakdown.

SUMMARY

It is safe to say that without good quality, Just-in-Time would crumble back into what most companies have always run, jokingly labeled "NIT"—or Never-in-Time. Quality is one of the essential ingredients, together with valid schedules and employee involvement, which can turn a Never-in-Time environment into a successful Just-in-Time environment. It is a matter of always striving to be better, and realizing that acceptable is never good enough.

As a primary component in the Just-in-Time approach, quality, with its focus on the return of quality to the source, statistical process control, and preventive maintenance, makes it possible to perform many of the techniques associated with Just-in-Time. In the chapter that follows we will examine another of the primary components that is equally responsible for the performance of Just-in-Time, valid schedules.

Chapter 7

Producing Valid Schedules

"CAN WE MAINTAIN VALID SCHEDULES IN THE FACE OF CONSTANT CHANGE?"

Parts come in, and finished products go out. Contrary to what some people may think, that is not the beginning and end of the manufacturing process. The first steps began months before when a company plotted out the year's course. Starting at the top of the organization the plans are laid out, stating the overall business objectives and how they are going to be attained.

Every company that plans to stay in business, whether they are making sophisticated and complex jet planes with tens of thousands of part numbers or simple widgets, must figure out what they intend to do, when they want to do it, and when it has to be done. Once that has been accomplished, they then have to be able to execute the plan. It is the most fundamental manufacturing concept. The logic is simple and straightforward.

Unfortunately, what may be obvious and logical is not always the course that is followed. There are many companies that are unable to accomplish these necessary steps. They are continually finding themselves up against the wall trying to squeak through the end-of-the-month crunch, running as fast as they can from one end of the plant to the other with hot lists and past-due work orders. They furiously call vendors over late purchase orders and stockpile those parts that arrive before they are needed. Then when it's time to build they find themselves with full storerooms, but mismatched parts. Why? Because they are unable to correctly plan what components they need when they need them. In other words, they are unable to produce and execute valid schedules.

If surprises are the rule, if mismatched parts are not the exception, if inventory is too large, and no one is being held accountable for the various problems, chaos is sure to follow. Trying to run Just-in-Time in an atmosphere like this is something akin to planting orange trees in the frozen north. You're not going to bear much fruit. It is essential to running the company that these problems be eliminated. Fortunately, as we mentioned in Chapter 2, there are a couple of ways to meet this objective.

Our experience has shown us that the challenge of manufacturing is not simply being able to plan and schedule but to be able to replan and reschedule. Planning is the vision, the ability to project into the future. Replanning is the response to reality, to what is actually happening in the marketplace and the company. The challenge for the company is to cope successfully with the multiple and interrelated changes that will rapidly cascade throughout the company. Internally, there are equipment failures, late deliveries, quality problems, and employee vacations or illness. Outside variables such as customers changing their minds, inaccurate forecasts, coupled with engineering changes, acquiring new equipment, and new product introductions all contribute to the complexity of this issue. In manufacturing the task is to devise the right schedule to represent the needs of the company, to maintain them as the needs change, and to ensure that the schedules reflect the capabilities of the company. The question for manufacturers becomes, Can we maintain valid schedules in the face of constant change? The answer is a resounding yes!

HOW ARE COMPANIES ACHIEVING VALID SCHEDULES?

There has been an impression that when examining what Japanese and American companies are doing in this planning and scheduling area, there are a great many differences. In reality, what we found was that there were more similarities between the two than contrasts.

It is important to note that even though Just-in-Time officially began under the auspices of the Toyota Production System, those companies doing the best job of creating a Just-in-Time environment in America, Europe, and Japan (Nissan and Tachikawa being two) are primarily using Manufacturing Resource Planning to handle their planning and scheduling, not those used in the Toyota system. What we will look at here is how both systems address the functions of planning and scheduling and which is most appropriate for a particular company.

THE FUNDAMENTAL MANUFACTURING EQUATION

Ever since people began building products, no matter what the environment and regardless of the type of product being built, there were four fundamental questions that needed to be answered:

1. What are we going to make?
2. What does it take to make it?
3. What do we have?
4. What do we have to get?

These four questions are as true today as they were years ago. The logic of these questions applies whenever and wherever things are being produced—whether they are jet aircraft, tin cans, machine tools, chemicals, cosmetics . . . or Thanksgiving dinner. How well a company answers these four questions determines how effective and reliable their scheduling will be.

Let's take a simple example. Word comes down that next Thursday the family is coming for Thanksgiving dinner. Thanksgiving already! The crunch is on. What do we need to make? Turkey, of course, but what would a turkey be without stuffing? The next step is to figure out what it takes to make stuffing. The recipe says we need a turkey, bread, butter, seasonings, onions, a stalk of celery, and four mushrooms. We go to the refrigerator to see what we have. There's butter, onions, celery, and bread, but no turkey, seasoning, or mushrooms. What do we need to get? Our grocery list then says, buy turkey, seasonings, and mushrooms, and have them at the house by Wednesday, just in time to start cooking Thursday morning.

The difference between planning and ordering the goodies for Thanksgiving dinner and scheduling and planning for a manufacturing company is complexity, and the fact that Thanksgiving doesn't get rescheduled. Thanksgiving is always the fourth Thursday in November, and its needs can be planned on the back of an envelope. The typical manufacturing company, though, has thousands of end items, 5000 to 50,000 part numbers, tens of thousands of bill of material records, thousands of routings, hundreds of work centers, and hundreds of vendors. In addition, change is constant. Customers change their minds, manufacturing processes don't work, and people are out sick.

If Thanksgiving dinner were dependent on those variables, you'd probably eat out.

The question which then arises is, How can a manufacturing company approach the complexity of these constantly changing scheduling problems? How does it attempt to solve the riddle of the fundamental manufacturing equation? Though there are a number of answers to these questions, most companies turn to Manufacturing Resource Planning, because it has been proven to be effective in any environment.

MANUFACTURING RESOURCE PLANNING

Manufacturing Resource Planning is more than a planning tool, it produces the schedules which say how to carry out those plans, and the elements necessary to execute those schedules. It also includes a feedback loop if things change and the plans and schedules can't be executed as originally set.

Many of the companies we have worked with that are successfully operating Just-in-Time didn't mention their Manufacturing Resource Planning systems. But we soon discovered it wasn't that they weren't using it. The situation was more that their system had become part of the woodwork: essential to maintaining the structure but so much a part of the daily operation as to be nearly invisible. It was there and doing its job. What more was there for them to say? To these companies the question of successfully running Just-in-Time without valid schedules was like asking, "Could you successfully run your company if you didn't have an accounting system?" Their Manufacturing Resource Planning systems are part and parcel of their process fabric. They couldn't imagine doing things differently. (See Figure 7-1.)

BUSINESS PLANNING

The Manufacturing Resource Planning process begins at the executive level of the organization. It is here that the business plan is established. This is where the overall figures for running a company are created, where income projections, costs, and profits are set out, and where budgets and cash flow figures are agreed upon. At Bently Nevada the entire management team meets once a month to formulate the business objectives and review how they are being achieved.

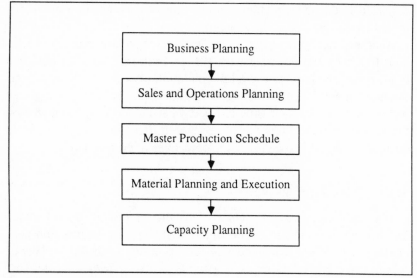

Figure 7-1. Modified Closed Loop

SALES AND OPERATIONS PLANNING

The next step in the process is to take the business plan and translate that into a sales plan and a production plan, which sets the overall level of manufacturing output. It is here that a company establishes its production rate to meet the needs of the business plan.

The top managers at APCOM meet monthly to review the previous month's progress and then adjust their plan to address the needs of marketing and the capabilities of manufacturing. At this meeting they will agree on the overall plan for the coming months.

MASTER PRODUCTION SCHEDULE

Once the business plans and the sales and operations plans are established, they must then be converted into a master production schedule. This represents what products a company plans to produce. This information is expressed in specific configurations, quantities, and dates. It is up to the master scheduler to create a plan which, ideally, satisfies the needs of the marketplace (demands from customer orders, forecasts, and distribution centers) while economically utilizing company resources (availability of manpower, equipment, and tooling). The companies that expect success with Just-in-Time put a great deal of emphasis in this area, particularly in addressing the need for maintaining a certain stability in the schedule.

Another important aspect of the master schedule is that it must be realistic. It should not be a wish list. If Tektronix finds their master production schedule isn't a valid simulation of reality, then it will be virtually impossible for them to determine what the material requirements are to make their product, and what the capacity resources of the various work centers are to produce it. This would also make it virtually impossible to support the objectives of Just-in-Time.

STABLE MASTER SCHEDULE

If any company constantly changes its master production schedule, introducing insignificant or unrealistic revisions, the factory and purchasing will be overwhelmed with the resulting reschedules. To run Just-in-Time efficiently requires a *stable master schedule*. To accomplish this they have established time fences in their master schedule. These points in time help handle how changes are managed. The closer a schedule comes to today, the more difficult it becomes to change it, whereas the further out from today, the easier.

The best results can be found when a company creates these time fences in the master schedule in three areas. The first should take place beyond the cumulative material lead time, where changes are handled fairly easily. The second area is the middle ground, inside the cumulative material lead time. Here, the execution of the material plan has already begun. This is the time when the master scheduler must begin balancing the changes that occur, attempting to reschedule as many dates out as he brings in, to offset the priorities. The third area is the short term. This is where changes are most costly to execute and therefore need to be avoided whenever possible, though this period can vary widely from company to company.

Hewlett-Packard's Vancouver facility has a fixed rate for one month into the future, with "a four-month freeze" on the master schedule on the up side—that is, during that time rates can't be increased. Even though schedules for products will change within the rates, this stability enables them to have very short material delivery times with vendors. Because their vendors have visibility and changes are managed, they are able to resupply H-P within two weeks.

In a Just-in-Time environment, these stable periods are also an aid for purchasing to work with vendors. By stabilizing the requirements, the vendors have an opportunity to hit the very small window of arrival necessary for Just-in-Time. If the master schedule were to be constantly changing in the near term, these windows would be totally unrealistic. This means the customer has to be able to give the supplier good visibility and valid dates. The burden in a Just-in-Time environment is placed on both customer and vendor to work closely on establishing these dates. The linkage that is necessary to achieve product flow is dependent on their ability to have an uninterrupted line of information.

Companies such as Bently Nevada feel that maintaining that kind of close-in stability would hurt them in the long run. They need to be extremely responsive to their marketplace. In order to do so, they are willing to accept the impact of these near-term changes to quickly respond to their customers' changing needs. Their solution to this problem is to have flexibility in the final assembly schedule, by adding as many options as possible at the end of the product build cycle, while stabilizing their master schedule at the level below final assembly.

One of the benefits of Just-in-Time has been that by reducing component lead times, a company can reduce their time fences. This means that a company will need less commitment out in the future and can be more responsive to changes that occur close in. In fact, an important part of the effort of continuous improvement is an ongoing reduction of each of the time fences. This must be established as a vital company goal, leading to faster responses to the marketplace.

MIXED MODEL SCHEDULING

Since bringing Just-in-Time on line, the Tennant Company has done a number of things differently that have improved their Manufacturing Resource Planning process. One highly visible change was to implement a technique called *mixed model scheduling*.

Prior to Just-in-Time, the conventional approach in most companies has been to "batch build" products to gain the cost advantages that have come with larger order quantities. The Tennant Company did this. With Just-in-Time, however, they initiated "mixed model scheduling" into their master schedule, which allowed them to minimize order quantities, while sacrificing neither productivity nor incurring extra costs.

Mixed model scheduling works like this. If there were three products being built—product A was 50 percent of total volume, Product B was 25 percent of the volume, and Product C the remaining 25 percent, a company would attempt to schedule these three each day as follows:

Day 1	Day 2	Day 3
A, B, A, C,	A, B, A, C,	A, B, A, C

Obviously, every other product is the popular one and the other two are interwoven.

There are two incentives for doing this, externally to the customer and internally to the factory and suppliers. The advantage externally is that by making products frequently you can offer quick delivery to the marketplace without having to carry a sizable finished goods inventory. Tennant Company reduced their customer response time by 80 percent when they switched over to mixed model scheduling. As an example, in the past, they built slow-moving products infrequently. These were made to customer specifications and when the time came to execute the master production schedule, Tennant Company would make only sold customer orders.

These orders were divided by the particular power type of engine, that is gas, electric or LP (liquid propane). They would build twenty gas engine cleaners the first week, followed by twenty electric the second week, and ten LPs the third week. If an order came in for one of their low-volume machines at the end of the third week, and that quantity in the master schedule had been consumed and/or the order arrived after this master schedule had been completed, the customer had to wait up to an additional four weeks before the cycle came up again.

What the Tennant Company was able to accomplish with mixed model scheduling was that they were always building what customers needed, rather than periodically building batches. They were able to do this by first reducing lead times and cycle times; the period it took to go from one model to the next was lowered from four weeks to less than a week. They believe this system has improved sales opportunities for them because of their better customer response time. (See Figure 7-2, Figure 7-3, and Figure 7-4.)

One of the requirements for taking full advantage of mixed model scheduling is the ability to make small order quantities and consequently quick change-orders in all areas, from final assembly all the way down through fabrication, including suppliers. Quick setups, lower order quantities, and frequent vendor deliveries are all primary elements

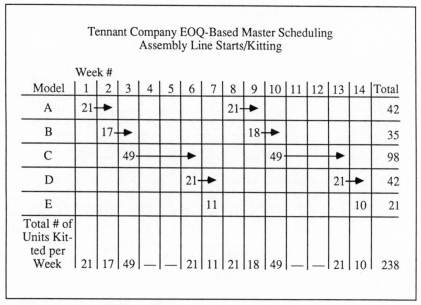

Figure 7-2. EOQ-Based Master Scheduling

Tennant Company EOQ-Based Master Scheduling Assembly Line Starts/Kitting

Model	Week # 1	2	3	4	5	6	7	8	9	10	11	12	13	14	Total
A	21→							21→							42
B		17→							18→						35
C			49——→							49——→					98
D						21→							21→		42
E							11							10	21
Total # of Units Kitted per Week	21	17	49	—	—	21	11	21	18	49	—	—	21	10	238

Tennant Company EOQ-Based Master Scheduling

Model	Week # 1	2	3	4	5	6	7	8	9	10	11	12	13	14	Total
A	17	4						17	4						42
B		13	4						13	5					35
C			13	17	17	2				12	17	17	3		98
D						15	6						14	7	42
E							11							10	21
Total	17	17	17	17	17	17	17	17	17	17	17	17	17	17	238

Figure 7-3. EOQ-Based Master Scheduling

of Just-in-Time. This smoothes the flow of parts throughout the factory. All are dependent on knowing what you want, when you want it, and where. If it is impractical to schedule all products frequently, in turn, it will be impossible to make and buy all components frequently.

Tennant Company
Mixed Model Master Production Scheduling

Model	Week # 1	2	3	4	5	6	7	8	9	10	11	12	13	14	Total
A	3	3	3	3	3	3	3	3	3	3	3	3	3	3	42
B	2	3	2	3	2	3	2	3	2	3	2	3	2	3	35
C	7	7	7	7	7	7	7	7	7	7	7	7	7	7	98
D	3	3	3	3	3	3	3	3	3	3	3	3	3	3	42
E	2	1	2	1	2	1	2	1	2	1	2	1	2	1	21
Total	17	17	17	17	17	17	17	17	17	17	17	17	17	17	238

Figure 7-4.   Mixed Model Master Production Scheduling

Tennant Company's Davis summarized his company's reasoning behind mixed model scheduling: "The need is to support irregular demands rather than use fixed order quantities based on average demands." The Tennant Company now breaks its final assembly schedule into days, attempting to cycle through all models within a week, (see Figure 7-2 or 7-3) using much smaller order quantities that are not fixed. To run this style of model scheduling also means that communication between marketing and manufacturing has to be good. The result at Tennant Company is "less inventory and better customer service."

MATERIAL PLANNING AND EXECUTION

In a Manufacturing Resource Planning system material is planned and scheduled via Material Requirements Planning. To accomplish this process, companies like Black and Decker and Omark use the information from their master production schedules, their bills of material, and their inventory records to calculate the material requirements to make the products they have planned. Material Requirements Planning does this through the computer system by calculating the right time to release new orders for material and then recommending the rescheduling of open orders to meet any changing requirements.

Through the introduction of Just-in-Time into the manufacturing process there has developed a spectrum of choices as to how a company can handle the execution of those material plans. Traditionally, this has been the province of the work order, which authorizes the building of the product. Work orders, though, need a certain amount of attention. They must be created, maintained through each work center, and then closed out when the work has been completed. In the context of the Just-in-Time environment, that generates a good deal of paperwork in two areas: issuing material to manufacturing, and tracking work as it is completed on the factory floor.

In an effort to relieve some of that paper burden, Black and Decker has been able to simplify or eliminate many of the transactions during the issue process. To accomplish this they have introduced a post-deduct technique after the product has been completed. This approach is only recommended when the criteria of short product build times and accurate bills of material are met.

Problems can arise with the post-deduct process if these criteria are not met. If there was an error in the bill of material, post-deduct could cause some real problems. For example, if components no longer being used were still showing up on the bill, then when it was time to post-deduct, the system would automatically deduct the old parts even though they were not being used. Obviously, the result would be inaccurate inventory records. By not deducting the components actually used, the on-hand balance for the substituted components would not reflect reality.

Black and Decker uses what they consider to be the purest form of post-deduct with their injection molding machines. The material goes from a 200,000 pound silo into a surge tank, and directly from the surge tank into a hopper. It's never touched by an operator. The stock is relieved only after the finished product leaves the department.

Since Black and Decker maintains bill accuracy in the 99 percent range and their products travel through the line in less than a day, they can effectively simplify their paperwork while continuing to generate the necessary work orders to support their scheduling system.

Omark has simplified the handling of work order tracking through the creation of a firm planned order, which records in the system that a quantity of pieces will be built without generating a work order for the factory. Though this firm planned order still needs to be closed out, there is no release of a work order in the system. Once the product is finished the components are again post-deducted.

Hewlett-Packard has taken this a step further by completely eliminating both the work order and the firm planned order. Instead they have instituted the use of a rate generator, which establishes within the system a fixed number of units to be built per day. They are able to utilize this approach because of their highly repetitive manufacturing environment. This should be the objective for those companies that are flow-oriented and don't have traceability requirements.

How a company chooses to handle their work orders is dependent on their specific environment and (as we shall see with the introduction of the demand pull technique) on how they decide to move material on the shop floor.

CAPACITY PLANNING AND SHOP FLOOR CONTROL

Capacity Requirements Planning calculates how much labor or equipment resources are required to accomplish the production tasks. This needs to be done far enough in advance to provide those resources.

The way to communicate and monitor how the schedules are actually being carried out is handled with a daily dispatch list. Dispatching is saying what the priorities are from the hottest job, the most pressing, to the coldest, the least pressing, by work center. This is the factory's "to do" list, and it is updated daily because things change.

Another one of the functions of Manufacturing Resource Planning in a nonrepetitive environment is to know where the jobs are. This is accomplished through tracking work orders. They say who has the item and who to send it to next. As mentioned previously, with the implementation of Just-in-Time, shop orders can often be eliminated in repetitive environments where there is a process flow because there's not the same need to track the item as closely as in an intermittent operation.

One way companies like Steelcase and Omark have been able to make changes in their dispatching and shop order systems is by utilizing cards rather than daily dispatch reports. For a number of repetitively used components, whenever a component is withdrawn by a demand pull system (to be discussed in greater detail in Chapter 8) they make more to replace what was taken. This approach requires no dispatch list, as it is a two-bin procedure. When the first bin is empty, this becomes the trigger to make more of the same item. For parts used frequently, this approach is simple, requiring no inventory record, and no shop paperwork. It is also effective because the correct items are being replenished. Many of the Just-in-Time companies using Manufacturing Resource Planning have found that in their most repetitive areas this technique has been an excellent approach to controlling line flow while reducing paperwork.

Steelcase, for example, uses Manufacturing Resource Planning to plan the total inventory of components necessary to support each line. The priority for when they build some of their components, though, is based on the use of a color-coded card system. Located on what they call their "scoreboard" are a series of part numbers and a predetermined number of cards (that come from Manufacturing Resource Planning) in three different colors. The cards represent each of the part numbers and how many containers of that part are to be built. As work leaves this operation and is pulled to the next operation, the colored cards represent how much inventory remains available. When a red card is visible it tells them they are almost out of stock on a part, a yellow card means they are going to be in trouble soon, and a green card says there's plenty of on-hand inventory.

By glancing at the board an operator can tell how many containers of parts are in process, how many he will have to produce, and when. As Rob Burch explains it, "Material Requirements Planning is our forecast, telling me in each week what quantity I'm going to need, and the card system tells me when to make it."

One of the issues we found was that few if any companies use one technique to address their planning and scheduling needs. Steelcase, for example, also has an area in their file plant where they order their materials by the order point system, simply eyeballing their stock. This involves a very limited number of parts and the process lead time is very short, making this scheduling technique adequate to meet their needs. Many companies have areas such as these in their plants where because of their extremely limited variety and their highly repetitive use, their planning and scheduling does not require the care and detail of a daily dispatch system or work orders.

Though Manufacturing Resource Planning isn't the only formal system for gaining control of a company's planning, scheduling, and execution, it is the proven system that can operate in any manufacturing environment, whether a company is an intermittent operation or a repetitive manufacturer. It should be mentioned, though, that in a repetitive manufacturing process, there are a lot less demands on a scheduling system once the master production schedule is established. In many of these cases, what is being built today is exactly what was built yesterday and what will be built tomorrow.

THE TOYOTA PRODUCTION SYSTEM

In addressing the needs of this particular repetitive environment another tested approach, which is part of the *Toyota Production System* should be discussed. The Toyota Production System is a compilation of many different manufacturing elements that deal with issues such as environment, quality, and setup reductions, as well as planning, scheduling, and execution techniques. What will follow is a discussion of those latter functions as to how they compare and contrast with Manufacturing Resource Planning. (See Figure 7-5.)

In the areas of Business Planning, Sales and Operations Planning, and the creation of a Master Production Schedule, the Toyota Production System and Manufacturing Resource Planning are identical. Where the two approaches go in different directions is in how they accomplish their material planning.

TOYOTA MATERIAL PLANNING

From a component scheduling standpoint, the Toyota Production System operates in much the same manner as a two-bin system, which is

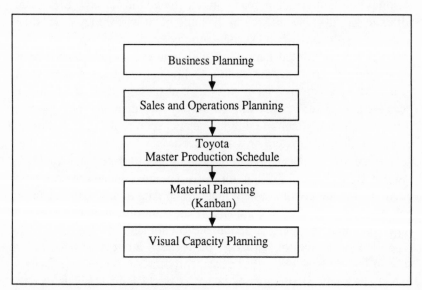

Figure 7-5. Toyota Modified Closed Loop

basically a reorder point approach. The two-bin system has been around for eons. The inventory is separated into two bins or locations. One is used to satisfy the need for that individual part, and as soon as that bin is empty, it triggers the replenishment of the part number. Until it is replenished, the second bin is used to supply the part. This approach requires no inventory data to be recorded either manually or by computer.

In the Toyota Production System the triggering mechanism is the kanban. Kanban, as we mentioned earlier, is the Japanese word for "visible record." But this is a bit of a misnomer since a kanban can also refer to a cart, or a square on the floor, or a golf ball, or a card passed between work centers. Though we will talk about the relationship between kanban and demand pull in Chapter 8, it is important to note that material movement in the Toyota Production System and the Harley-Davidson approach is handled only via kanban. Kanban also tells them what they are going to make, since in the kanban/two-bin approach, they are essentially replacing what they have already made. The presumption is, if you have used up your inventory, you will need more. Because this is not always the case, Harley-Davidson and others have instituted the use of a black kanban marker to indicate an obsolete or changing part that should not be replenished.

It must be realized, though, that there are certain criteria necessary to operate under a two-bin system to avoid running into some major problems:

1. Lead times are known and fixed.
2. Past demand equals future demand.
3. Demand is going to be constant, not irregular.
4. There are not conflicting priorities.
5. There is no need to look out beyond the current order cycle.

If these criteria are met in a manufacturing process, the order point system is a valid candidate to produce the necessary schedules for the company.

Toyota has taken four very important steps to ensure that these prerequisites are met:

1. They employ a mixed-model master schedule.
2. They use small order quantities.
3. They have short lead times.
4. Capacity planning at all work centers is straightforward due to flex-

ible machinery, cross-trained operators, and a steady flow of material.

THE TOYOTA MASTER PRODUCTION SCHEDULE

The combination of limited varieties of models, high volume, and mixed model scheduling enables Toyota to ensure that the future resembles the past. In their master production schedule, Toyota schedules the same products, not only every month, but within each week, and in turn, every day. This is possible only when a company is making a highly repetitive product and has quick changeovers. Without this environment, the kanban cards would be replenishing the wrong components—the components used today would not equal the components needed tomorrow.

By scheduling every product, every day, in a sequence that intermixes all products each day, all components are being consumed and all are being replenished. Moreover, all components that are being replenished will be needed.

SMALL ORDER QUANTITIES

The second way the Toyota Production System handles potential order point problems is by using extremely small order quantities. The ultimate manufacturing goal is for the production rate to match the sales rate: Use one, make one, and sell one. The combination of making products repetitively, as well as in very small quantities, causes a continuous demand on all of the lower level component parts.

SHORT LEAD TIMES

The third aspect of the Toyota Production System is the use of very short lead times. An order point system does not identify the need to reschedule. If lead times are short, the work-in-process is small, and changes become easy to implement.

It should be mentioned that there is a primary limitation in using the kanban approach: It provides no visibility into the future. This has led Toyota to perform a bill of material explosion which gives their managers and suppliers a ninety-day forward visibility by taking the requirements for each product and summarizing the need for each component.

INFORMAL CAPACITY PLANNING

Because the master schedule generates the need for a steady, repetitive flow of parts, capacity planning at all work centers is fairly straightforward and can be done informally. The burden is on both the factory and the vendors to gear up to handle any increased or decreased volume in the master schedule.

Without the simplicity of this feature, the surprises caused by manufacturing a wide variety of parts in a nonrepetitive manner would make this job extremely difficult unless calculated through a computer. This is not to suggest that the Toyota Production System is a computerless system. Toyota is a highly computerized operation, as are virtually all successful Just-in-Time companies.

SUMMARY

What we have seen is that both Manufacturing Resource Planning's and Toyota Production System's planning and scheduling elements are the same in their objectives: recognizing the need for valid schedules and providing a system to maintain them. Both systems place a great deal of emphasis on front end planning—that is, establishing the business plan, developing that into a comprehensive sales plan and a production plan, and then creating a realistic master production schedule. Where the two systems differ is in the material planning area. The interesting factor here is that the basic functions of material planning are the same in both Manufacturing Resource Planning and the Toyota Production System, and the differences lie in the techniques for achieving it.

How then does a company choose the right system? The answer to this question depends solely on environment. The Toyota Production System has shown itself to provide valid schedules in a highly repetitive environment. With it, the material planning and control activities are largely done without recording inventory data and therefore operate inexpensively. Manufacturing Resource Planning can also operate effectively in a repetitive environment but it requires additional transactions. This extra information is of increasing value when products are sold intermittently or are non-standard.

Selecting the right tools for planning and scheduling and using them properly are far more important issues than worrying about which label to attach. Furthermore, the distinction between one approach versus another becomes blurry as companies use the best parts of both. The common goals are better control of the business, being able to run simulations, improve vendor performance, eliminate end-of-the-month crunch, reduce expediting, improve quality, reduce costs, and respond quickly to customers. In the next chapter we will discuss how the technique of demand pull operates in the plant.

Chapter 8
Demand Pull

Just-in-Time challenges every function of the plant environment, but few of its techniques are as highly visible as the material movement aspect called *demand pull*. As mentioned in previous chapters, demand pull has had a significant impact on the control systems for the shop floor. Demand pull is an excellent approach for material movement through the line operations when needed, no matter what planning and operating system a company may employ.

Demand pull is a consumer-initiated material movement technique, which allows a downstream work center to pull material from the preceding upstream work center when it is needed. The execution of this downstream demand becomes the authorization for the upstream work center to make more. Demand pull answers the question of when to make something. In this case the "when" is the physical transfer dictated by the downstream work center's need.

If that sounds simple, that's because it is. One of the primary reasons for using the demand pull technique is that it is so simple. It also offers an effective approach to controlling outbound queues, the material that has been completed but not yet moved to the next operation. No more material can be worked on when the outbound queue is full to its authorized limit. Only when material leaves the outbound queue can the operator make more.

There are basically two ways of reducing the size of this queue, first by simply beginning and then addressing the problems that may surface, or second, like the scuba diver described earlier, dive below the surface and fix any problems with quality or flow prior to beginning. We recommend an approach that progressively controls queues first, limiting the amount of work between each work center.

Once this has been done and the problems eliminated, then set up a

111

demand pull line. Having satisfied these first two steps, a company can then switch from pushing material down the line to pulling it.

There are a variety of ways to use demand pull, most based around kanban-type signals to authorize movement. As explained in Chapter 7, kanban has become the generic name for a number of different techniques. In its simplest form demand pull uses a line of linked operations so that each feeding operation can see when the downstream work center needs more material. While this approach may be the easiest to run, demand pull can be operated very effectively through the use of cards, squares on the floor, or carts. Instead of the trigger being an empty space between work stations, it can be an empty cart containing a group of items as used by the Tennant Company, or a card that signals the need to make more as used by Omark, Steelcase and Harley-Davidson, or an empty square on the floor like at Hewlett-Packard. The reasons these methods are used depends on whether the feeding station can physically see the downstream work center, or on the size of the items being built, or the size of the order quantities being produced. Interestingly, the least important aspect of this process is the triggering mechanism for moving material. Many first-time observers have a tendency to get caught up in the cards, squares, golf balls, or carts and lose sight of what the real issue is—communicating a need. All these methods essentially will achieve the same results.

There has been some confusion as to whether demand pull can be used to control what part number each work center will make. This is a separate issue from when the work is performed. As explained in Chapter 7, the two-bin system says replace what was used. The Manufacturing Resource Planning system would say, schedule to need. It is important to make this distinction, because there are some highly repetitive companies like Toyota and Harley-Davidson that use demand pull to move material and to tell them what they will make next— that is, use one, make the same one. Most companies, though, use demand pull as solely the consumer-initiated material transfer/movement technique which triggers the authorization to make more.

As an example, in the demand pull operation at Hewlett-Packard the product being built is driven by a schedule, which plans ahead and does not simply replace what was used. In this particular instance, both H-P's final assembly operator and the first work station operator receive a daily schedule, so the operators know the sequence in which to build. This scheduling is necessary to accommodate the proper mix of product build. Knowing the sequence allows the operator in the first work center to begin only what is needed, and the operator at final assembly to complete what is needed according to schedule.

No matter how a company decides what to make, in all demand pull systems the only time an item or component is moved is when there is an expressed signal for one. If there is no demand coming from a downstream consumer, then nothing is produced. At Hewlett-Packard, if the choice is producing more simply to replenish inventory or to stop producing because none is needed, they would prefer idle operations to excess inventory. This may be an overly simplified explanation, but one which clearly illustrates how it controls the size of the queues in the shop.

Nissan is another excellent user of demand pull. At their plant in Murayama, Japan, Nissan has six million square feet of manufacturing space, with 6600 employees. They produce 30,000 cars and 1600 forklifts per month, and their master schedule performance is 99 percent on time. Nissan turns their inventory in this assembly plant a little less than once a day. They produce those figures with the aid of Manufacturing Resource Planning telling them what to make, and by moving the material on the shop floor via demand pull.

Harley-Davidson, in its highly repetitive system, utilizes a three-card demand pull for their system. They refer to this as the MAN system, or Material As Needed. The first card is a raw material card, which authorizes material to be moved to the first operation. The second card is a production card, which allows an operator to start building. This card contains both the container size to be used (Harley works with standardized containers) and the quantity of containers to be produced. The third card is a move card, which authorizes the movement of finished parts. All production cards are placed on boards near the various work stations. They are in turn controlled by green, red, and black markers. Green signifies that the part is currently being produced. The red marker says it's time to build. The black marker is the hedge against the two-bin system making what is not needed since it signifies that this part should not be replenished at this time.

For ordering materials from vendors, Harley simply mails the raw material cards to its suppliers, having already worked the mail time into the system. Currently, when a supplier receives a predetermined number of cards it triggers a delivery with the cards attached. This is similar to the approach used in the Toyota Production System.

When the proper conditions are met the advantages of demand pull are numerous. First, it's simple to operate and easy to maintain. If a problem arises with the items on the line and we want to stop production because all the demands are tied together, the whole line can be shut down in lock step. This can be particularly helpful if a quality problem surfaces, or someone is having a problem with a specific aspect of the process. Everyone's attention is immediately focused on the problem, and they can all work toward solving it.

The conventional approach to moving material in the factory is to move it as soon as it is ready to the next operation. This is called the push system. The feeding operation then works on the next scheduled job. Typically, in a push system the feedback loop is much longer than with demand pull, so the process might continue building and piling up inventory at a bottlenecked work center. With a demand pull system the flow is immediately stopped until the problem work center is cleared. This stoppage can be communicated to everyone along the line by the use of a light, sign, or some other signaling device.

Another advantage of demand pull is that it allows a company to maintain visual capacity controls. Omark, which uses a card as their triggering device, is able to adjust their capacity by "massaging" the cards, either subtracting or adding cards. To make sure that everything runs smoothly, Omark has moved their planners onto the shop floor so they can visually see which operation has which parts. As Omark's Kevin Donigan points out, "Anybody can look up on the kanban board and tell by the number of tags how many pans are in the system and where they are, because each operation has a given amount of tags, and you should have the same amount of pans (of material) at each operation. Either you're going to have a tag or a pan of parts. It flows."

Though demand pull does not in and of itself reduce queues, it does help a company to do so. Omark went into each operation and asked, "What's the least we can run, but still watch costs?" Once those standards were set, work could accumulate only to those levels. For example, in their zinc plating operation, the fewest number of pans they can run so the parts aren't overprocessed is three. The operators have to have three cards before they can perform the operation. Prior to lowering order quantities and implementing their demand pull line, they thought the bigger the run the better, so it was not unusual to find the aisles piled with queued inventory.

In addition to the obvious benefit of less space and less money tied up in inventory, another contribution a company gains by reducing queues is that the lead time of items is greatly reduced.

In the chapter that follows, we will look at some other techniques that will improve the process flow of any company, whether or not they are running demand pull. These techniques include cellular manufacturing, process-sensitive product design, and line balancing. All of these techniques allow each employee in the Just-in-Time process to realize that there really are no unsolvable problems once they have been given the right tools to do the job.

Chapter 9

Product, Plant, and Process

"MANUFACTURING AND (PRODUCT) ENGINEERING HAVE TO WORK
HAND-IN-HAND FROM THE CONCEPT STAGE WHERE IT'S EASIEST TO
PUT IN CHANGES, RIGHT ON THROUGH PRODUCTION."

The aim of Just-in-Time is to make a company's immediate needs.
The test for this is that a company is on the verge of consuming those
parts. The nature of the process should be a synchronized flow where
raw materials are converted into components, and components into
products, and then the products go out the door just when the customer
needs it. The objectives are then to reduce manufacturing lead times,
taking cost out of the product, and utilizing all of a company's resources effectively to produce more in the same amount of space or
less. This is also an effective way for a company to increase production
without increasing space.

A good place to begin the process of addressing these objectives is
by examining the physical flow of materials and components. By simply drawing a map of the plant, it is easy to trace the routing steps
necessary to build a single product. Once this has been done, it is
immediately evident what is really happening with material movement. At Black and Decker (see Figure 9-1) the flow chart of the original power cord process is anything but flow-oriented. Operations are
spread out from one end of the facility to the other. By creating this
simple chart of part movement, companies such as Black and Decker
have been stunned by the distance the product travels and the amount
of nonvalue-adding activities such as material handling and queuing
these processes included. Black and Decker has now completely redesigned the layout of this area to make the flow much smoother using a
technique called *cellular manufacturing.* (See Figure 9-2.)

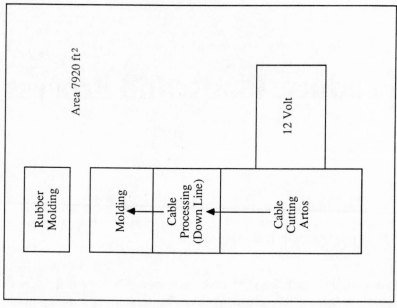

Figure 9-2. Material Flow Diagram After Linking

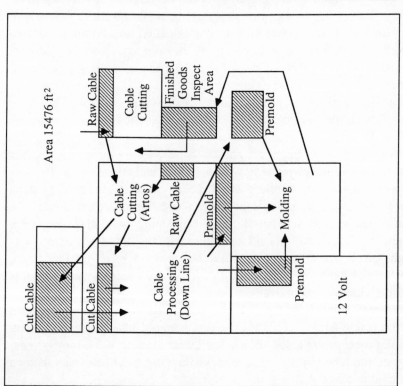

Figure 9-1. Material Flow Diagram Before Linking

CELLULAR MANUFACTURING

Cellular manufacturing is the linking of operations according to their various part families, and likeness of manufacturing process, as opposed to the more traditional groupings of machines according to functional capability, such as drills in one department and lathes in another. Some companies create cellular manufacturing units to form a complete production operation, from raw material to finished part, subassembly, or product.

This was the theory behind Black and Decker's redesign. The process originally was made up of three different departments: the Artos, which cut and stripped cable; the processing line, which hank-tied the cable, stripped the leads, and applied the terminals; and the molding department, which attached the plugs. Typically, the Artos production would take place three to five days prior to the cable traveling down the processing line. The inventory produced would then be stored, taking up about 1000 square feet of space in various locations around the shop. By linking these three operations into a direct line, Black and Decker saved roughly 3200 square feet. (See Figure 9-2.) Essentially, there is no work-in-process inventory between the three operations. Once they start cutting a reel of cable, they will have finished products within an hour.

They put virtually no money into this revised operation. Everything used already existed in the plant. The only costs were manhours to move equipment into the straightened line. Clarence Bauer was the department manager who worked with the supervisors and operators to install Black and Decker's power cord line. As we had mentioned earlier, his feelings about what Black and Decker was able to accomplish were quite evident when he said, "When you are all done, if it doesn't look as if you should have done it years ago, it may not be the right solution. After we completed this, we kept asking why in the world didn't we do it this way before? It makes absolutely no sense to have done it any other way."

Though they did put some money into other linking operations, with some equipment retooling and the addition of fifteen feet onto their cordless drill assembly lines to accommodate subassembly operators, these investments have paid off. They are now producing more in two shifts than they used to produce in three.

Besides the increased productivity and the inventory reduction, Black and Decker also increased their inventory turnover from 20 to 35 per year and slashed lead times from days to a few minutes, while increasing the quality of the product. They also realized the added bonus of freeing up 3200 square feet of valuable shop floor space. In spite of its value to the company, the space issue was actually not part of the original reasoning for linking operations—improved flow of materials was.

The process of cellular manufacturing is dependent on three main prerequisites.

LINE BALANCE

This means that the capacity required to do the job at each step in the cell is equal to the demonstrated capacity of each station or piece of equipment in the line. There are times when this can be a problem, especially when one piece of equipment in the cell runs considerably slower than the rest. But as the Tennant Company pointed out in their cell assembly lines, it was not necessary to slow the faster machines because often times the slower operations were able to pick up the pace. Line balance is extremely important to be able to reduce queues and subsequently reduce work-in-process.

SHORT SETUP TIMES

As we discussed in Chapter 5, reducing setup times allows a piece of equipment the flexibility to make a small quantity and thus a wide variety of parts. This achievement enables it to be switched from part to part quickly to keep up with the mix of product in final assembly or components in fabrication. Of course, if a cell has equipment dedicated to doing just one job, setups aren't a factor.

ECONOMIC FEASIBILITY

If equipment is dedicated to a cell, then cellular manufacturing makes sense only when the volume of a family of parts is high enough to sustain the cell. It is for this reason that companies that are thinking of buying new equipment for use in a cellular layout should think about smaller and simpler machines.

The Tennant Company began their cellular process by straightening the flow of operations and then bringing subassemblies directly onto the assembly line. Subassemblies used to be built on the far side of the plant. They were then put into stock and brought up to the line as needed. Obviously, this added a level of inventory that was costing them money and taking up space. By making the subassemblies on the line they eliminated the storage racks that were filling up the floor, as well as the double handling of material that took place when they were returned to stock before they were needed.

Their work cells were also designed to give them the flexibility to go up and down with demand. These cells are capable of producing between three and seven cleaning machines a day, simply by moving people in and out of each cell. This brings up the importance of a work force able to meet these flexible needs. Cellular systems are more effective if operators are cross-trained and can move from one manufacturing process to another as the need demands. Together with their mixed model scheduling, the Tennant Company is now able to go from frame to crated product right on the assembly line. They are also finding that they can build machines in fewer hours than they ever were before, even with added operations.

One of the techniques the Tennant Company has used to help cut down on space and to improve communications among the operators was to install three *U-shaped* assembly lines. By creating U-lines, they have been able to bring the people on the line closer together. This, of course, has also brought the operations closer, so if a problem comes up, everyone can be involved more quickly to help solve it.

Interestingly, after taking these steps they have discovered, according to Duane Davis, that, ''There are very few products at Tennant Company that can't be built faster than it takes the paper work to go through the system.''

By bringing some of their subassembly operations directly to the assembly line, Black and Decker also achieved some significant results. One area in particular that gained by this move was their battery pack production. It once took 15 welders to produce 1500 battery packs a day, but by putting this subassembly directly on a paced assembly line, they were able to do the same job with four operators producing 2700 a day. This has saved Black and Decker about $50,000 a year. They have also been able to reduce the work-in-process on batteries down from over 2000 to 100. On the success of this project, Black and Decker is now putting more and more subassemblies at their final point of use.

Cummins UK moved their operations to a cellular format and reduced their travel time by 97 percent. To do this, though, took a great deal of resource. While some companies were able to accomplish their move to cellular manufacturing with little cost, a major plant rearrangement can cost a company millions of dollars when it comes to moving giant presses or furnace operations. Cummins got around some of the rearrangement cost by installing automated guided vehicles that move material via a track on the shop floor. Nonetheless, cellular arrangements can be costly, though in many cases the costs are far outweighed by the reductions in lead time, floor space, and inventory.

Cellular manufacturing was a primary ingredient for Steelcase's Just-in-Time approach. They took directly to heart the idea that every time you touch a part and don't add value, you are not being efficient. They instituted a pilot program, moving three brake presses together to form a cell, with each press dedicated to a particular step of the process. This was the most expensive aspect of their decision, both in terms of actually moving equipment and the dedication of equipment. Typically, one machine would run an entire order through an operation, then move them to the second machine, and so on. Steelcase had a damage rate running as high as 60 percent, with tremendous work-in-process. By switching to a cellular approach, and using a demand pull system to move the material from press to press, it improved their quality by 80 percent and cut lead times by almost two-thirds.

FLATTENING THE BILLS OF MATERIAL

To continue the trimming of fat from every step of the manufacturing process, bills of material are slowly being consolidated as subassemblies find their way onto assembly lines. (See Figure 9-3 and Figure 9-4.) The sequence is to structure the bills of material to reflect the process as it presently exists. Then if the process can be changed by reducing the steps, the bills of material should be changed along with it.

As the bills of material are flattened, less paperwork and fewer inventory transactions result. Since fewer work orders need to be issued to cover the various production levels (in some cases they can be completely eliminated) scheduling is made easier. As regards to Manufacturing Resource Planning, with inventory reduced and the routings condensed, scheduling becomes easier and more easily controlled.

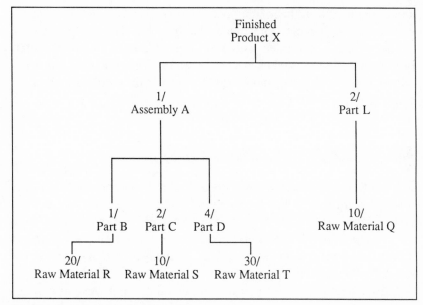

Figure 9-3. Typical Bill of Material

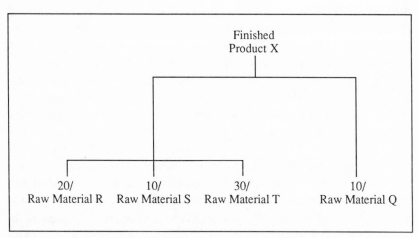

Figure 9-4. Flattened Bill of Material

Black and Decker has done a lot of work to flatten their bills of material, which has been reflected in their lead times. Their bills were originally structured in such a way that for every level in the bill they had a one-week lead time, and the planners would adjust those figures in scheduling items out. But since they have gone to a Just-in-Time approach, they have been able to shorten and reduce lead times in the manufacturing process. This means that their Manufacturing Resource Planning system is loaded with almost no offset for lead time. Additionally, Black and Decker has been able to flatten their bills of material with nothing going below three levels. Many bills are, in fact, single level.

PROCESS-SENSITIVE PRODUCT DESIGN

In order to fully utilize the concepts of Just-in-Time, product engineers often have to design the product differently. They need to take into consideration every step of the manufacturing process to make sure there are no wasted moves. By considering every step, the engineers are able to see if any can be combined or changed to make the product easier to manufacture.

A good example of an engineer's significant role in designing product for cells was offered by Tektronix. After redesigning their printed circuit boards and linking their PC line, they have reduced their lead time from thirty-three days to three days from raw material to finished product. The product as a whole has been redesigned to be manufactured in a constant flow. Because the lead times are now so short, there is no longer a need to store large batches of these items. This has allowed Tektronix to eliminate completely the stockroom where these boards were once stored.

The Tennant Company was also able to simplify their manufacturing process through the efforts of their design engineers. They consolidated some of their sheet metal components into single molded parts with a simpler structure capable of providing the same function. They were able to reduce the number of parts from around 2000 down to 800. Because they now had fewer part numbers being produced at the same volume of production, it then made it economically feasible to manufacture them in dedicated cells.

Another aspect of this sensitivity in product design was accomplished at the Tennant Company by adding product options as final assembly options, rather than having them two or three levels deep in the bills of material. At one time, they had put the higher percentage options on the machines and then reconfigured them, pulling them out of stock and disassembling them according to the customer's need. Both of these product redesign examples were the result of engineering coming to manufacturing and saying they could do a better job of dealing with parts, process, and inventory by designing new concepts that were sensitive to manufacturing.

Bently Nevada believes wholeheartedly in this cooperative approach. They, too, were trying to speed up their circuit board operations. Their answer was to move their circuit board engineering offices near the production floor, rather than isolating them in some secluded corner. These designers became an integral part of the process. But the main issue at Bently Nevada was as much the testability of the product as their ability to build it. Because they make devices responsible for measuring the variations in giant turbines, they have to be able to assure the accuracy of their devices.

The usual process as described by Bently Nevada's design engineer Jack Opocensky was "engineering would design the product for the optimum engineering principles, which meant the minimum number of components and the simplest and neatest way for it to work. Testability requires you to go back and put in nodes that you would not put in for engineering purposes. You are adding components, which is the opposite of what you are trying to go with from an engineering aspect." To make this new approach effective, both engineering and manufacturing had to work closely together to assure that "testability" was designed into the product. As mentioned earlier, in Bently Nevada's case, engineering gave manufacturing a percentage of space on the PC board dedicated to their particular needs. This simple joint effort allowed them to reduce their testing times from forty hours down to *eight* minutes on two different products!

As Opocensky said, "Manufacturing and engineering have to work hand in hand from the concept stage, where it's easiest to put in changes, right on through production. If you start after the product is designed and tested, and prototypes are built, it's a real costly stage to start putting in testability."

SUMMARY

Any company implementing process changes should start with the layout of process flow. Once they see how their product travels through the system, they can begin to examine cellular manufacturing to see how it can work in their environment. The next step is to check product design and, by working as a team, see if the product can be made easier to manufacture, more process-sensitive. At the heart of Just-in-Time is continuous process flow: eliminating the detours commonly found in process routings and shortening the path to finished goods. The tools and know-how are accessible. The challenge is, too.

The next direction on the Just-in-Time journey is the road to better vendor deliveries and improving vendor relations. Operating Just-in-Time will make little sense if suppliers don't properly understand the needs and repercussions of delivering late or stockpiling inventories to guard against this possibility. The responsibility for bringing the supplier on board is the customer's. But as we will see, this is good news, because the benefits the customer reaps from establishing these excellent vendor relations is excellent vendor performance.

Chapter 10
Excellent Vendor Performance

"ADVERSARIAL RELATIONSHIPS AND JUST-IN-TIME DON'T MIX; THEY WORK DIRECTLY AT CROSS PURPOSES."

American manufacturing has traditionally fostered a unique working relationship with its suppliers, based loosely on the Leaden Rule (the opposite of the Golden Rule): "Do unto others before they do unto you." This is not to imply these actions are either intentional or taking place on a one-way street. Many suppliers own a share of guilt for substandard performance. But in trying to meet the needs of that age-old saying, "The customer is always right," they have frequently found themselves being expedited up one factory aisle and down the next. They have been pitted and played against other vendors in the name of competition, and taught to take nothing for granted.

Though the onus for this deteriorating relationship is not solely on the customer's shoulders, the ball is clearly in their court to change it. In most companies if buyers don't have several suppliers for the same item, and don't go out and rebid the prices for that item every year, they are liable to be biding their time elsewhere. From an upper management point of view, to have one supplier and give them all the business is probably against corporate policy. The stated reason for this protective behavior is simply that you can never depend on a single vendor. One of them will always let you down. This is why Xerox used to carry over 5000 suppliers. And why suppliers of companies like Xerox could never really invest the money they wanted into their plants—because they were never quite sure they were going to get the business again.

Another major factor that has contributed to these negative multiple relationships has been that vendors have had to labor under the unnecessary burden of poor scheduling. Without proper visibility into their customer's needs, they are once again up against hostile odds to satisfy demand. This creates a state of having to constantly expedite the customer's needs, which then pushes the customer to multiple suppliers to make sure his needs are covered. Of course, poor scheduling is also a two-way street, with customers having to suffer vendors' unreliable schedules.

The requirements of Just-in-Time have led companies to take a different approach. Instead of the traditional adversarial relationships, they have laid the groundwork for long-term relationships with their suppliers by establishing multiyear contracts, assuring them that the business is theirs. The other part of the deal is that vendors will deliver according to the schedule exactly when it is needed. This gives the vendor security and the customer flexibility and, hopefully, lowered costs. In fact, these companies have been *encouraging* their vendors to come on board in this fashion for some time now.

This does not mean that a customer goes to a supplier and says, "I'm going to run Just-in-Time, and you're going to have to live with that." The vendor will read that as nothing more than a directive to run a large batch, store it, and then divvy it out everyday. To Xerox's Pierre Landry, this is definitely not the answer. "If we have reduced delivery frequency from two weeks to daily," he says, "but all it means is that the supplier is still holding all the inventory, we have accomplished nothing. Whether it's inventory on our side or on his, we are going to pay for that inventory."

In order to bring vendors on board for Just-in-Time, companies have to lead by example. They must have implemented successfully some of the elements of Just-in-Time into their process. They should have active programs addressing quality, setup reductions, dependable schedules, and order quantity reductions. "If you're not prepared to do what you're asking the vendors to do," says the Tennant Company's Duane Davis, "don't expect much back. This is especially true if he says, 'I want to do it, but I don't know how.' " By following their own advice, the Tennant Company received price reductions from their vendors of between 5 and 10 percent. They have also been able to change their buyers from expediters to what they call "vendor managers." These are people who work closely with a supplier, making sure the supplier understands Just-in-Time and its special needs. The difference the vendor manager has made really hinges on the notion of establishing a trusted working relationship.

This is one reason why the company that wants to do Just-in-Time needs to have their own house in shape first, so they will have something worth sharing with their vendors. This will also help dispel some of the mistrust from vendors who fear Just-in-Time is another one-sided customer ultimatum. The task is to build a long-term relationship. To do so, both sides need to relate to each other with respect and dignity. Three notes help form such an accord between vendors and customers:

1. Trust.
2. Continuity.
3. Consistent signals.

PROVIDING VALID VENDOR VISIBILITY

The natural place for vendors and customers to build trust, continuity, and consistency to deliver Just-in-Time is through the solid foundation of valid scheduling. Providing a vendor with reliable visibility of present and future demands allows a supplier to better manage his business. Without this visibility, a vendor is reduced to guessing, left to try and forecast to fill the future void, which results in added costs and added lead times. Forecasting can be completely eliminated once the customer can provide valid long-range plans.

This is where the technique called "vendor scheduling" takes firm hold. By giving the vendor valid schedules broken down in weekly or smaller time periods, and extending this through an agreed-upon number of periods, a supplier can clearly see what a customer needs and when. The vendor can then build to that schedule. A number of successful companies using Just-in-Time use the Kanban card to authorize shipments. They pull from vendors in the same way as many of them operate the physical movement within their factories. There is a natural marriage between the information that Manufacturing Resource Planning provides and the goals of Just-in-Time. MRP II gives the vendor valid schedules and good forward visibility and helps reduce the paperwork associated with purchase orders, change orders, and follow-ups. (See Figure 10-1.) Xerox provides their vendors with material requirements planning reports, which they stressed were of the utmost importance to making their vendor programs function as well as they do.

These schedules are the bridge to Just-in-Time, allowing a vendor to know what is needed and to deliver, just when it is needed. Many companies that have been running Manufacturing Resource Planning

Jones Company vendor schedule for: Smith, Inc. — week of 02/01/8X

Vendor #114

Vendor Scheduler: AB
Buyer: CD

Firm Zone: first 04 weeks   Material Zone: next 06 weeks

··········· Requirements ···········
FFFFFFFFFFFFFFFFFFFFFFFFFF MMMMMMMMMMMMMMMM

Item #	Description		Week 2/1 & previous	Week 2/8	Week 2/15	Week 2/22	Week 3/01	Week 3/08	Next 04 Wks	Next 12 Wks
13579	Plate	Qty:		100				100	100	300
		PO#:		B1146						
24680	Panel	Qty:	20	20	20	20	20	20	80	340
		PO#:	B1122	B1146	B1180	B1203				
42457	Tube	Qty:	300			200			1100	3500
		PO#:	B1122			B1203				
77543	Frame	Qty:			40		40			
		PO#:			B1180					

Figure 10-1. Vendor Schedule

before implementing Just-in-Time have found that vendor scheduling has already initiated closer working relationships with their vendors. So as Just-in-Time reduces the number of vendors involved, Manufacturing Resource Planning is refining those relationships by offering clarity and reliability for what is needed and when.

How much information should a customer share with its vendor? Black and Decker supplies their vendors with as much information as they desire. "We will give them five weeks," says Ken Good, "we'll give them five months, or we can give them a year. It's the only way to operate, especially where you have single-source vendors, and they've got to come through."

Historically, one of the greatest paybacks of a Manufacturing Resource Planning system has come in the area of vendor scheduling. Since a company is providing reliable schedules, this valid visibility allows a vendor to do away with their just-in-case inventory, plus the cost of expediting and unplanned overtime. This, in turn, reduces a great deal of their costs. Surveys have shown that by implementing vendor scheduling, Manufacturing Resource Planning users have seen a substantial reduction in the price of parts and raw materials. Combined with their Just-in-Time efforts, these reductions have become even greater.

Hewlett-Packard has established through their scheduling system a link between their crating suppliers and their packing suppliers. H-P has arranged for the crating vendor to deliver his materials to the packing vendor, who applies the packing and then delivers it, just in time, to Hewlett-Packard.

As discussed in Chapter 7, much of the credibility of valid schedules in Just-in-Time comes from the notion of stability in the master production schedule. These firm commitments are usually for periods of fifteen to thirty days. During this time a company agrees with the supplier that "This is what we will buy from you," followed by perhaps sixty days in which they say, "This is our best guess as to our future needs." Obviously, this makes the demand on the vendor much more predictable. It also translates into greater vendor stability.

Omark believes the best way to develop trust is to stabilize or "freeze" the master schedule. This gives the supplier a fixed target to aim for rather than one that is constantly changing. This commitment then allows Omark to ask for smaller deliveries, more frequently, because they have accepted the arrangement that during the freeze period they will not cancel, reduce, or increase their order. This makes the vendors a lot more amenable to Omark's needs. The turning point, though, is Omark's up-front commitment, and their *willingness to stick by it.* Normally, their master schedule freezes are for two-week periods.

Even with this stability, Omark still feels it has some flexibility. If they really need something within that firm period, they are not adverse to asking. It is for this reason that we refer to these times as "firm" periods in the master schedule rather than frozen. The truth of the matter is, when an important customer calls his vendor and asks for help, even though the rule says the schedule is frozen, the vendor will invariably help out. The concept is basically the same, but "firm" is a term a little closer to reality, implying that a company is doing its best to strive for stability.

In spite of those times when the best laid plans go astray, consistency and continuity are still the mainstays for building trust. Vendors learn quickly when a company demonstrates through actions its good intentions. When a schedule is given, they know it will be adhered to close in, and changes at this time will be the rare exception rather than the rule. This allows the Just-in-Time approach to take hold. Once schedules are reliable, a customer can begin working with a vendor to make deliveries at specific times during the workday. Properly choreographed, these delivery windows can be the difference between running Just-in-Time, or operating Never-in-Time. When scheduling vendor delivery windows it is important to start broadly, and then slowly notch the window times down.

Hewlett-Packard has developed four-hour windows with some of their vendors. These suppliers have a proviso in their contracts which states that if three times within a year these vendors miss their delivery windows, their contract with Hewlett-Packard can be renegotiated, and the vendor may therefore lose H-P's business. Needless to say, it is not necessary to schedule such narrow delivery windows with every vendor. Those who deliver cleaning supplies, for example, may not need to meet such strict daily schedules.

If a company can give their vendors consistent and honest signals as to what they need and when, and work together, then Just-in-Time can do its job well. But it is in trying to establish these company interfaces that companies often get lost in the tall grass. Black and Decker found the trick was to bring their vendors into the process and make a point of communicating with them. In so doing, they received very little resistance. "You can't make a case not to do Just-in-Time," explains Black and Decker's Ken Good.

Omark, already having established their vendor relations with valid schedules, took the next step. Realizing the importance of their suppliers understanding their business, they brought the vendor's manufacturing people into their plant to spend a couple of days working out on the floor with Omark's operators. The idea was that by letting the vendor see how their material was being used, they would be more sensitive to Omark's needs.

Xerox organized trips to Japan, taking their vendors to see first hand what was possible, and what the competition was up to. The key strategy behind these trips was the development of mutually beneficial long-term relationships, or vendor partnerships. To accomplish this they established a Top Management Communication Interface, a group of Xerox's top management who would meet with their suppliers' top management, annually, to discuss Xerox's needs and their vendors' concerns.

Establishing trust with a vendor is a slow, continuous process. Courting these relationships requires more than words: It requires action, tangible evidence of a company's sincerity. Omark's Mark Bletscher, supervisor of Allied Production and Inventory Control, believes building this kind of credibility with a vendor is much like treating them as part of the family. "If you treat them like they are another department in the operation," he says, "then you will have their input. But if you tell them, 'If you don't deliver, we are going to cut you off tomorrow,' then you are operating from a position of fear instead of a position of commitment." Adversarial relationships and Just-in-Time don't mix, they work directly at cross-purposes. This is why companies are hard at work reducing their vendor bases and providing valid schedules to better establish relationships built on commitment rather than fear.

BRINGING THE VENDORS ON BOARD EARLY

One approach Just-in-Time companies have used to gain a vendor's commitment is to bring them on early in the Just-in-Time implementation process. Prior to this, a company's purchasing people will need to be involved as the process gets under way, at least as observers, because it won't be terribly long before they will be carrying the Just-in-Time message to their vendors.

The Tennant Company has found this early supplier involvement really pays off. They are eager to show their vendors anything and everything they can. Black and Decker has much the same approach, sponsoring annual vendor days. Vendors are invited into the plant and shown all operations. They are told about the state of the business, what Black and Decker's plans are, and what new products will be introduced. At the end of their first vendor day, they handed each supplier an envelope with specific and individualized requests, such as a commitment not to increase prices or a request for daily deliveries. This individual treatment drew a tremendous response from the vendors. These days quickly became a regular part of the way Black and Decker does business.

Xerox, with 80 percent of their manufacturing business conducted with vendors, believes wholeheartedly in early supplier involvement. They established Multi-Functional Commodity Teams, which were responsible for managing a given group of suppliers. They were also involved with the suppliers, working from design through development on new components. This close relationship was fostered to implement the most cost-effective designs possible.

The first step Xerox took in this process was to co-locate some of their purchasing people with design engineering. They believed that by bringing their buyers into the conceptual phase of development, they could then better translate Xerox's needs to their suppliers.

To illustrate how effective this early involvement can be to a product, Pierre Landry tells about a project that Xerox thought was doomed to extinction. It seems a competitor had come out with a great product very similar to what Xerox was planning. Xerox dutifully assembled their key suppliers together, who had been involved in the designing of the Xerox product, and told them they felt there was no sense in continuing based on the success of the competition—unless, of course, they could come up with any ideas on how to improve the design and costs.

The suppliers went to work. One found he could eliminate cost on some plastic parts. Another found a way of redesigning a component here, another there. As Landry described it, ''The next thing we knew we had a program again. The suppliers' contribution to the design was essential to assure quality, costs, and delivery.'' He then added that the suppliers willing involvement was, of course, not totally altruistic. ''If we meet targets and they meet targets, then we will give the supplier a guarantee of production orders for the life of the part. As with the guy who helped us with the plastic parts, we wrote a contract that says, 'you're it.' ''

This kind of proprietary relationship demands trust between the customer and the vendor. And though Xerox has their vendors sign nondisclosure agreements, what really builds trust, Landry believes, is living out their pledged commitment and leading by example.

The process doesn't have to stop there. Hewlett-Packard stressed an interesting concern: It is not only important for them to involve their suppliers, but they also have to see to their suppliers' suppliers. H-P feels that if their suppliers' suppliers weren't looking toward running Just-in-Time, too, the system would eventually run into problems. Their point is, the catalytic effect from customer through suppliers ultimately improves all operations, from raw material to finished product.

VENDOR EDUCATION

As we discussed in Chapter 3, education is where excellent vendor performance becomes a reality. Xerox has an extremely active supplier improvement program. Their objective is simple: to have their suppliers adopt Just-in-Time. From their own experience, they know full well the impact Just-in-Time has on quality, lead times, and subsequent delivery, as well as the effect these procedures should have on costs.

They provide two seminars that each of their vendors must attend. The first is for senior managers, to introduce them to the process. This is a one-day miniseminar, an orientation for the decision makers of Xerox's suppliers. In some cases this is the president of the company; in other cases, for larger suppliers, it would be for the division vice-president. These seminars let the supplier know what Xerox is doing. They outline the narrowing competitive gap that they are confronting with Japan in hot pursuit. They detail the commitment they are making to manufacturing. They then give an overview of the Just-in-Time approach. As Landry describes these sessions, "By the end of the day, better than 95 percent of those decision makers are convinced there are some real opportunities for them in Just-in-Time manufacturing."

Xerox then sets up the next phase with those vendors, which is a more detailed three-day seminar on the specific how-to's of Just-in-Time. These seminars are attended by people, such as the manager of the production operation, the manager of manufacturing engineering, and the managers of quality control or materials. Three people from each supplier are invited for this in-depth program.

At the present time, Xerox has trained over two hundred of their North American and European suppliers, all of whom have gone through the full educational cycle.

As a follow-up, Xerox did a survey of their suppliers after they had gone through the education process. They found that 50 percent of the companies had begun Just-in-Time operations in their plants, and another 45 percent had started some sort of internal education, like quality circle-type meetings. Only 5 percent of the companies involved had not made any changes, which made it quite clear to Xerox the lack of interest these companies had in working closely with them.

SHRINKING THE VENDOR BASE

Trying to build a foundation of trust with a large force of vendors is economically impossible. Trust is a long involved and evolving process that must be continually worked on. The only feasible answer is to have fewer vendors.

Having a smaller vendor base makes a lot of different things possible. For one, it significantly alters the role of the buyer. Hewlett-Packard is no longer interested in having buyers in the traditional sense. The image they want is not buyers, but vendor managers. These are people who develop a close relationship with a supplier, which allows them to focus on issues other than placing purchase orders. If a vendor manager has 100 people to talk to instead of ten, his ability to be effective is greatly diminished.

Besides the improved communication aspects, the benefits of reducing the vendor base for those suppliers still involved are great. They know that the company is still buying the same volume of product as before, but now, instead of sharing that volume among 100 other suppliers, it will be distributed to one or perhaps a few. Suppliers also enjoy the benefits of the customer's experience in implementing successful techniques for lowering order quantities, reducing setups, and reducing inventory. This can have a profound impact on vendors, allowing them the ability to offer lower costs on smaller order quantities, while producing more with greater efficiency.

Even though the objectives of vendor base reduction must be tailored to meet the needs of each individual company, there are certain criteria that each company needs to consider. Past delivery performance, reliability, price, quality, labor stability, and vendor proximity all should be considered. Black and Decker's objective is to single-source their suppliers whenever possible. In moving toward this, they have gone from 400 vendors down to 250 at their Tarboro facility.

Consolidating suppliers in a multiplant environment can be a night-mare. Xerox was faced with this problem on a worldwide basis. Since their largest manufacturing concern was in their copier, or reprograph-ics division, they began their consolidation process there.

The first thing they did was to centralize their commodity opera-tions. They appointed a vice-president of materials management and had all the materials managers throughout the system, who had been reporting to their various plant managers, now report to this central VP. Selection and management of the suppliers is done by the Central Commodity Management Group. The local plant management author-izes material releases against contracts negotiated by the central group. This was the only way Xerox felt they could get a handle on the vol-ume of vendors with which they were dealing.

Once Xerox had established this system, they began the laborious, yet essential, process of supplier selection and negotiations. They es-tablished commodity teams made up of the senior buyers from all of the plants, quality people, and cost engineers. Then it was a one-at-a-time examination of the vendors, weeding out the late suppliers, sub-stantiating figures, exposing poor quality vendors, or whether or not a vendor was investing in new technology. The process took about two years.

The vendors who survived the process were then brought into the contract phase. Obviously, the relationship between these suppliers and Xerox had changed substantially. Xerox was interested in long-term cooperative relationships, which became very appealing to the suppliers, who found they were being contracted on jobs for world-wide requirements. This made discussions over pricing easier, and it made talking about quality issues essential.

The next step was the education process, as mentioned earlier. This gave the suppliers a clear understanding of the importance of what they were being called on to perform. It was here too, that if Xerox found a supplier was unable to deliver what he had promised, the amount of Xerox's future business was usually more than enough to get the sup-plier's needed attention.

Some of Xerox's suppliers were not immediately convinced that Xe-rox had all their ideas neatly stacked together. They couldn't believe that something like setup reduction in the magnitudes they were talking was possible. One such skeptical supplier was converted when, with Xerox's help, they reduced the setup of one of his machines from twenty-eight minutes to eight. He became so enthused, he then figured out how to lower the setup down to a minute!

IMPROVING VENDOR QUALITY AT THE SOURCE

In Chapter 6 we spoke about the importance of establishing good vendor quality programs. Again, the significance is of the utmost concern. The savings companies have realized by insisting suppliers initiate vendor source inspection are truly substantial, especially in the area of reducing receiving inspection. This is where statistical process control has been a real boon. As previously mentioned, Tektronix used to have 100 people inspecting incoming merchandise, but today, because of their vendor quality program, they have one!

As evidence of how far Tektronix has come with their vendors, each day a vendor arrives with several carts filled with crating material. He brings the material right onto the shop floor, puts it away where it is supposed to go, enters the receiving transaction on Tek's system, and then stops by purchasing and tells them what he brought. They hand him a purchase order and a release number, which makes the process official, and he is on his way. Typically, very few companies would trust a vendor to bring his deliveries directly into the plant, let alone enter the necessary transactions into the computer. But because they are certain of his quality, and the relationship they have built, it's now the most natural of processes.

Quality issues are so important to running a Just-in-Time operation that a company has to be willing to roll up their sleeves and really go to work with their suppliers to solve their problems. Often times this means leading them down the learning curve. This is why it is also so important to reduce the vendor base. What suppliers must understand is if incoming inspection is being eliminated, and if the vendor is shipping junk, they will be shutting down the customer.

CREATING THE ELECTRONIC LINK

Since Just-in-Time is the elimination of waste, and paperwork, as we have already discussed, does not add value to the product, any way to effectively do away with paperwork is a plus. Xerox has accomplished this by creating an electronic network with their suppliers. In an effort to shorten lead times even further, they have currently hooked up, via computer, 115 of their North American suppliers. Through this linkup they transfer order releases and receive back shipping notification as soon as the supplier has shipped the order. The vendor is provided with the ability to access Xerox's main data base, and can make inquiries into the status of purchase orders for reconciliation problems, payroll, and other concerns. A company needs nothing more than a personal computer to be able to be part of the network, and in some cases Xerox has even provided those. (See Figure 10-2.)

Xerox has also begun a pilot with their vendors for electronic invoicing. Since they've got the contract on file, the order release, the shipping information, the quantity, and date, the vendor can issue an invoice, computer to computer, back to Xerox. This is one way of dealing with the impact on accounting departments often caused by Just-in-Time. We will explore these issues a little later in this chapter and in greater detail in Chapter 13. For now, Xerox's electronic network offers a way to reduce vendor lead times, and vastly improve trust and communication.

There is an excellent example how of how an electronic system can really make vendor deliveries work. A rather unique relationship exists between two Class A Manufacturing Resource Planning users in Japan: Nissan and Tachikawa Spring Company.

As mentioned in Chapter 8, Nissan's Murayama plant produces 30,000 cars and 1600 forklifts per month. Their inventory is not measured in months or weeks, but in terms of days—3.5 days in the press department, 0.5 days in the body department, and 0.9 days in final assembly. Their delivery lead time to domestic customers is 6 days, and they are meeting 100 percent of their delivery commitments.

To achieve that success, Nissan chose a Manufacturing Resource Planning system over a kanban-based approach for two reasons. First, where Toyota has Toyota City with vendors clustered in the immediate area, Nissan's suppliers were further away. They felt that the Toyota Production System would not work as effectively under these conditions. They believed the way to bridge that problem was by communicating with their long-distance vendors via schedules rather than by a kanban card. The second reason was that Nissan didn't want to simply replace what they consumed—they were interested in bringing in what they needed.

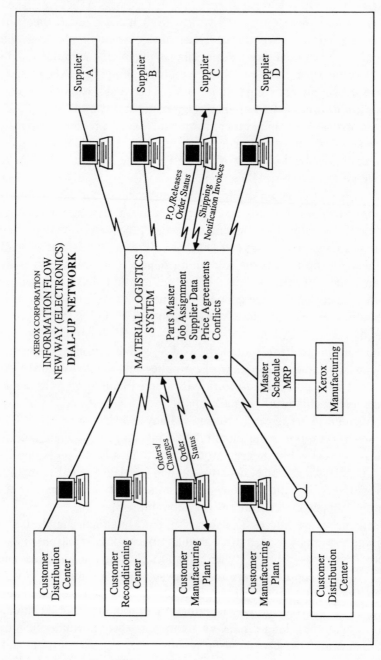

Figure 10-2. Xerox Electronic Data Link

For example, if they built a car that had white bucket seats, but the next dozen cars did not, why replace white bucket seats merely because they had used them? The alternative is scheduling white bucket seats the next time they are needed. Manufacturing Resource Planning would schedule it, kanban would replace it.

This procedure takes place between Nissan and their supplier, Tachikawa. Tachikawa also has a Manufacturing Resource Planning system. They supply Nissan with 80 percent of their seats, though Nissan is not their only customer. They produce 200,000 seats per month.

Every three months Tachikawa receives a rough schedule from Nissan. Then every ten days they get an update of that schedule, and finally they receive a schedule every two hours of the various seats and styles, which they ship to Nissan hourly. This information is calculated by material requirements planning from the Nissan Manufacturing Resource Planning system. In turn, Tachikawa takes those requirements and feeds them into their Manufacturing Resource Planning system to generate schedules of what components are needed when. This drives their operating system. Three hours after receiving their final schedule from Nissan their products are delivered to the Nissan factory. A Tachikawa truck leaves for the Nissan plant as soon as sixteen seats are ready for delivery. These seats are loaded in the exact sequence that, when unloaded and put on the Nissan conveyer, will mesh with all the other components required to make that specific vehicle. Tachikawa carries no finished goods inventory.

Nissan relays their needs electronically to Tachikawa, computer to computer. They call this process synchro-scheduling: synchronized arrivals, coming together at the right time at the right place, with exactly what is needed, all handled via two Manufacturing Resource Planning systems. The process benefits both sides. Nissan not only receives deliveries in sync with their operations, but the system allows Tachikawa to turn over its inventory *84 times a year*. The key here is Nissan's excellent schedules. Their return is excellent vendor performance—a rather dramatic example of how effective Manufacturing Resource Planning can be in a Just-in-Time environment.

REDUCING PURCHASE COSTS

In attacking the size of the vendor base, one would think that pricing might be a major consideration. Lower prices, though, are not necessarily the driving factor: Better deliveries, better quality, and deliveries in smaller quantities have a more favorable impact than a possible increase in price. Even so, there is little justification for the implementation of Just-in-Time by a supplier to increase prices. What it will certainly do is reduce purchase costs, which is significantly different from price. Obviously, when a company is operating with less lead times, less inventory, reduced setups, and knowing exactly what they want and when, the overall cost of purchased items is going to go down. If a customer has worked closely with a supplier to improve these areas, or even if a vendor has done the work on his own, it will allow the supplier to lower his pricing. Xerox makes it clear to their vendors that they are not after their profit margin, but if costs have fallen, they do expect to share in that savings.

The reasons for high costs can come in a variety of forms. Xerox discovered, through their program of benchmarking against the competition, that they were paying 40 percent more than a Japanese competitor for plastic parts from the same supplier. They discovered that 25 percent of the overage was in the cost of raw materials, the resin. This discrepancy was rather amazing to Xerox since resin is a petroleum by-product and there is no oil in Japan. The question was, How could a Japanese plastic supplier pay 25 percent less for his raw materials? The answer was that the Japanese pool their requirements, buying up gigantic quantities of raw materials at a great savings. Xerox has begun a similar operation, pooling all of their plastic suppliers and then negotiating contracts with resin manufacturers for their suppliers.

Another 25 percent of the cost increase was due to overhead rates, and the other 50 percent was due to design. The differences from the Japanese in design were broken down into cosmetic and appearance. If Xerox designers wanted black resin, any discoloration or scratch would not be accepted. So vendors would buff out all marks, and if there was a black part that had a white streak in it, they would reject the part. But in reality, if that part was underneath the copier, nobody should care about the discoloration. There were also differences in the thickness of the plastic. American plastic parts weighed almost twice as much as the Japanese. When Xerox distilled the kinds of resins the Japanese used, they found six different types, as compared to their twenty-three. Also, as mentioned earlier, where Xerox would design a highly sophisticated multi-functional, high-cost, plastic part, the Japanese would utilize the principle of compensating tolerances, and produce a number of very simple, cheaper metal parts.

The results they obtained produced a 50 percent reduction in product cost, which is significant but not good enough for Xerox. The Japanese are still spending 20 percent less.

KEEPING THE LID ON TRANSPORTATION COSTS

Another factor in the price of vendor products of special concern to Just-in-Time manufacturers is transportation. If a vendor is making small quantities and shipping frequently, a customer could be very quickly eaten alive by the high freight costs. The saving grace has come in the guise of freight consolidation.

Freight consolidation involves the use of public carriers, not only to deliver but to consolidate. The consolidation process involves a variety of vendors delivering their daily output to a central point, typically a carrier's facility. Each day, then, the carrier consolidates these many less-than-truckload deliveries into a full truckload and delivers to the customer. Carriers are hungry for this business. Thanks to deregulation, they can now go after it. Hewlett-Packard and Xerox are both doing a great deal of freight consolidation.

By doing so, they have learned to deal with their carriers in a similar fashion as with their vendors:

They have fewer carriers, having reduced their carrier bases.

They have recognized the need to educate and train their carriers about the Just-in-Time approach and related transportation requirements.

These companies have also instituted bus routes, or milk runs, for their suppliers. In Hewlett-Packard's case, they have contracted with a freight company to pick up daily from some of their out of the way vendors, on a prescribed "milk run" route.

Xerox has similar bus routes running in the Rochester, New York, area and in greater Chicago. Within a forty-mile radius of their plant in Rochester a Xerox truck will make a daily, and punctual, scheduled pickup.

The general manager of one of Xerox's suppliers absolutely loves the consistency and continuity this bus route gives him. Everyday, this general manager goes out to lunch and returns around 1:30. Instead of parking out front at that time, he parks in back and walks through receiving by a particular place on the shipping dock. Overhead is a little sign that says "Xerox—5 Part Runs." He knows his assembly line is running sixty of each of those parts a day, and he also knows that he better see 60 each of those five parts when he comes back from lunch, because at 3:00 PM sharp the Xerox truck arrives to pick them up. If the general manager doesn't see them, instead of going to his office, he'll go to the foreman and find out what is happening. It makes the process incredibly simple for him, and very visible.

His people also like it. They know that every day there have to be 300 parts on the dock, and they have to be good parts. When those parts arrive at Xerox's Webster facility, they go directly from the dock to work-in-process, with no inspection.

Building excellent vendor relations like this can be extremely important to a company, especially when acts of God strike, and they are suddenly faced with another insurmountable opportunity. Bently Nevada's Ray Bacon was up against just such an act. Bently's plants are located in Minden, Nevada, at the base of the High Sierras, about a thirty-minute drive from Lake Tahoe, surrounded by 8000–12,000-foot mountains. A particularly heavy snow and rain storm cut off the valley where Bently Nevada's plants are, and there were no open roads into the area from the west, which translated to no deliveries from the west.

Of course, Bacon had a supplier in California whose route over the mountains was completely sealed off. The reports from the transportation department regarding opening the roads were bleak. Bacon needed the parts or his operation would be crippled. Because of the relationship he had fostered with his vendor, he was told that the supplier was more than willing to send a truck out on a Sunday over a 900 mile detour around the Sierras to bring in the needed supplies. Within hours of the dispatch of the long journey, the highways were cleared, and the problem averted. Nonetheless, the vendor felt he was a partner of Bently Nevada's and would therefore be willing to do whatever it took to get the supplies delivered. The key issue here is that in a Just-in-Time operation a vendor's responsibility increases when delivery is critical. This is one of the things a vendor agrees to when they become part of the process.

GEOGRAPHIC DESIRABILITY

The spot that Bently Nevada found themselves in is one created by having to use vendors outside of the close proximity of the plant. In this case Bently Nevada is in such an isolated area, that *everybody* is far away, but other companies may not be so cut off. Geographic desirability is an important issue for Black and Decker. The majority of their vendors are within close range of their Tarboro, North Carolina, facilities.

Hewlett-Packard's Greely, Colorado, plant is in much the same predicament as Bently Nevada, yet they are receiving daily air shipments from suppliers in Japan. As we mentioned earlier, where a supplier is located in respect to its customer may be of special concern when deliveries are required every couple of hours, but there are times when that just is not necessary, or possible. Xerox has even worked out a system with their Japanese suppliers to receive parts on a weekly basis, and they have not had a problem operating Just-in-Time with this system.

But as the saying goes, "There is more than one way to skin a distant cat." One step Xerox took to speed up foreign deliveries was to have the U.S. Customs Department declare their Webster facility a free trade zone. This reduces the customs delays and added expenses often associated with off-shore suppliers.

The principle for Xerox is still, though, that the best supplier is the closest supplier. They will, in fact, let a local vendor be as much as 15 percent higher in cost than Far East suppliers if their quality is as good, in order to reap the added advantages of their geographic proximity.

These far-sighted approaches to vendor transportation issues on Xerox's part may make perfect sense, but things were not always this way. At one time, all vendor deliveries were shipped to their Webster facilities. They would be inspected and then reshipped to their plants around the country. What finally convinced them of the folly of this operation was a supplier in Los Angeles, California, who would ship his product to Webster as directed, only to have Xerox ship it back across country to its facility in Irvine, California, about forty miles south of L.A. Today, Xerox has solved this problem with direct part shipment to its manufacturing sites. The reason for this is that today parts no longer need to be inspected!

IMPACT ON ACCOUNTING

One of the areas often the hardest hit by a Just-in-Time effort is the accounts payable department. Though we will look at overall accounting procedures more closely in Chapter 13, they do impact vendor-customer relations, especially as more frequent deliveries become the norm. Some companies can receive as many as three shipments a day from a supplier. Separate purchase orders for each receipt would cause a flood of paperwork, drowning both purchasing and receiving people as well as vendor accountants.

Obviously, changes in accounting procedures need to take place to handle Just-in-Time deliveries. One approach might be to receive daily and to pay monthly. Xerox's electronic network is another answer to curtailing the paperwork involved and allowing for the accumulation of the daily data. Though, currently, this method of accounting is still in its pilot stages.

As with buyers, it is important that accountants are also brought into the Just-in-Time process as early as possible, to try to combat some of the problems that will inevitably arise. It is far better to have an accountant as part of the team from the onset, adding his input and airing his concerns, rather than trying to patch together accounting answers after his life has been made more complicated by daily deliveries and daily invoices.

MOTIVATING A WIN-WIN PARTNERSHIP

Most vendor companies' immediate perception is that Just-in-Time will mean more work for them in the short-term. It's getting them to realize the long-range benefits that can really bring them on board. Therefore, it becomes imperative for a Just-in-Time customer to let his suppliers know that they are all in this process together. They also need to realize that anything the vendor does to make the customer more competitive will increase his competitive edge as well. The operative phrase is *win-win*.

The advantages of such a partnership should be quite evident. Some of these are:

1. By a customer's consolidation of their vendor base, a supplier will be getting a greater share of the business, while the customer will receive added control over their purchasing dollar and potential reductions in cost.
2. By a customer's commitment to a long-term relationship, a vendor will be able to plan for next year more effectively. The customer

benefits equally in this partnership arrangement by building a positive trust factor, which is the vendor's assurance that the customer will get what they want when they want it.

3. The survival factor—if the customer is successful, the vendor will succeed. Of course, in this case the reverse is also true.
4. By being able to supply Just-in-Time, it will improve a vendor's own competitive ability. If they can sell their products to his customers with better quality, shorter lead times, and more frequent deliveries, at a better price, other companies will find their services equally attractive.
5. By bringing the supplier on board, the customer can eliminate the nonvalue-adding costs of incoming inspection.

Omark has had little trouble convincing their vendors of the mutual advantages to be found in operating Just-in-Time. In fact most of their suppliers are more worried about keeping up with Omark, rather than having to be pushed to cooperate. Those vendors have also found that by becoming vendor partners with Omark in this process and committing themselves to the work, they are also meeting the needs of their other customers better.

Of course Xerox has found the power of the win-win relationship to also hold true. On a recent visit to one of Xerox's trained suppliers, Pierre Landry was proudly shown a machine cell a vendor had set up under Xerox's impetus. Creating the cell had reduced the lead time on the part from seven weeks down to three days! Unfortunately, Landry recalled, it wasn't a Xerox part. But then he was pleased to find out it wasn't a competitor's part either.

SUMMARY

The benefits of Just-in-Time extend to all who come on board. By establishing close, working, and trusting relationships with suppliers, by providing them with consistency and continuity, forces can be joined together to produce a manufacturing economy fit to fight the battles of the world marketplace. And of course, win.

Chapter 11

The Marketing Edge

"OUR MANUFACTURING PROCESS IS HIGH PERFORMANCE. IT'S FAST TRACK. IT'S SHORT LEAD TIMES, ON-TIME DELIVERY, AND LOW COST."

What surprised many of Xerox's suppliers was how potent Just-in-Time is as a marketing tool. They realized how competitive it had made their production process, but many of them hadn't considered what it could to for sales. Sure, Xerox had advocated Just-in-Time as a manufacturing savior, an unequaled opportunity to make them all more competitive in the face of global competition, but what these suppliers really hadn't expected was the fallout.

When a company is more competitive, when their product and process is consistently demonstrating the highest quality, when they can offer and deliver on shorter lead times, and when they can deliver to a customer exactly what is needed when it is needed, it won't take long before marketing and sales can use the good news to get more orders.

Typically, the problems that surface on the shop floor end up being the problems of marketing and sales. Products that aren't made on schedule can't be shipped on schedule either. One company where this was once a problem was Ilsco. There was a time when Ilsco was known as a company that manufactured a high-quality product but never delivered on time. "We had a terrible delivery record—maybe 20 percent of items shipped on time," Dave FitzGibbon, Ilsco's president admits. There were chronic shortages of high-volume "bread and butter" items so important to sales. Embarrassed sales representatives had to spend selling time fielding phone calls from anxious customers demanding to know the status of their already overdue orders. FitzGibbon recalls handling two or three of the most irate calls personally on a daily basis.

Now at Ilsco there are no more apologies. When commitments to customers are being met, nobody is happier than marketing. Salesmen say they have time to do the selling they were hired to do, now that they're no longer expediting several hours a day. Marketing executives say they have the time to watch the sales territory better, evaluate the sales force, and look at new markets. They can plan advertising campaigns with confidence, certain that the advertised goods really will be available.

The president's phone is also a lot quieter. FitzGibbon reports just one or two times a quarter that he is called in to troubleshoot. "Sometimes I even get a little bored," he says. Ilsco's VP of marketing, Bill Dulle, has noticed the difference too: "It's sort of like being a Maytag repairman," he adds.

Rather than spending their time apologizing for long lead times, late deliveries, and poor quality, Just-in-Time frees up marketing and sales to do their job. When the complaints have stopped, and marketing and sales can proudly advertise, "We are a Just-in-Time supplier" and then deliver on that claim, they have set the standard. Being the best and being able to do it for less is a powerful selling tool.

That's the end result. How and when a company involves its marketing people in Just-in-Time is a return to the fundamental structure of the process. This means bringing marketing in as early as possible. Like all other departments, marketing and sales need to be educated in the objectives of Just-in-Time, and involved in the preliminary presentations and discussions prior to any pilot implementation. Marketing needs to understand the whys behind producing products more often and in smaller quantities. Bently Nevada's Joe Shull even believes marketing and sales "ought to be involved with product structure strategy. They ought to be involved with manufacturing lead time cycle strategy. They ought to be involved in looking through product routings and finding unnecessary queue times and unnecessary work-in-process inventory, so they understand how the product is built and exactly what the costs are." This is the same educational process that manufacturing goes through. By bringing marketing into the process early, it allows them to make the program their own, too. This avoids the roadblock that can arise if marketing sees Just-in-Time as being a manufacturing program that is simply being handed down to marketing. Early involvement also allows marketing to fully understand their essential part in the process: to get their customers to order more frequently and in smaller quantities so the company can build only what is needed when it is needed.

Ah, but there are those in marketing departments around the country who are probably cringing at the thought of smaller order quantities, and what that will mean to price breaks and a company's ability to ship on time. There are salesmen out there whose blood runs cold when they hear that Just-in-Time is reducing inventories. They see their ability to serve the customer quickly draining with the smaller stocks. Their first reaction then is to fight the process. But if a company educates their sales and marketing staff first, lets them in on the reasons behind the changes, and also begins changing their attitudes as well, then real progress can be made.

CHANGING ATTITUDES

So much of the implementation of Just-in-Time depends on people willing to change. Marketing is no different. They have to really believe that Just-in-Time will benefit the company, the marketing department, and eventually the customer. Even though most companies implement Just-in-Time as a way to reduce costs, the one who ultimately benefits is the customer. If marketing doesn't develop this attitude, if they see Just-in-Time as something that management has thrust on them, telling them to go sell it, then there will be problems. This means an appropriate education, and a proper voice in the planning process. "They have to believe it's going to help them sell," says Bently Nevada's Shull. "If they believe that, they'll go out and make it into a sales pitch."

To do this, marketing must understand how these Just-in-Time issues are a selling point. First, since quality has to be better to produce in reduced order quantities, the customer will be receiving a higher quality product. Second, with reduced product build times, lead times are reduced, offering more flexible and responsive deliveries. When a customer wants something they often want it as fast as they can get it. By building products more often and in smaller order quantities a company can be more responsive to the needs of the customer. If changes occur shortly before shipment, a Just-in-Time supplier might be able to be more responsive to that need. Third, with less rework and reduced inventories, costs on a long-term basis will be lower. A company can then pass on some of those lower costs to the customer.

MARKETING'S INFLUENCE ON JUST-IN-TIME

But this is not a one-way street. Marketing does not just benefit from Just-in-Time, it also brings its own influence to bear on the subject. APCOM proved that when their marketing department began dealing with one of their major customers, by offering to do *their* inventory control for them. As APCOM's Don Rice explains it, "They don't call us every week and say 'here's an order,' they call us every week and say, 'here are our inventory balances,' and then they give us a list of what they intend to use. Our responsibility is then to make sure that they have what they need to produce what they want. So instead of them just ordering and putting the order into inventory, they call us up, and say 'this week this is what we have, and this is what we intend to use.' " APCOM then plans and produces to support their needs.

In an effort to accommodate their Just-in-Time operations, APCOM's marketing, working with manufacturing, suggested this arrangement to the customer. When the customer had attempted to provide this information themselves, APCOM was very disappointed in the results. The customer never had a good handle on what they needed. They built inventory to cover themselves, and then, not too surprisingly, they would find they were in an excess inventory situation. When this took place they would immediately stop buying from APCOM. "That created a real dark area for us," Rice said from his Tennessee office. "We never knew when they were building excess inventory or when they were running low and needed something. All we knew was when they ordered. So, we got into a situation where we were watching their demand and we didn't know if their demand was dead on or under by 10 percent or over by 20 percent. There were a number of times when we thought it was a normal demand month and they ended up having excess inventory so they would not buy anything."

Since the customer had no facility to provide valid vendor schedules, APCOM explained the problem to them, and suggested another alternative. If they would share with APCOM their inventory information, APCOM would watch it and guarantee they didn't have excess inventory. They also told them they would guarantee that they would provide the customer with whatever they needed to take care of their production demands.

As Rice added, "What has happened is we have reduced inventory levels for our customers significantly. Our largest customer used to carry anywhere from eight to twenty-five weeks of our product on hand. We've reduced it, and now they have from two to four weeks of inventory on hand as a maximum. When it gets to four weeks we don't send them any more, but it offers us a buffer to work within, and we can do our planning from that." Without marketing's influence, it would have been virtually impossible to operate this phase of Just-in-Time. It was essential to the process that marketing establish a consistent demand rate.

This is exactly what Xerox's marketing department was able to bring to their Just-in-Time efforts, the ability to respond to short term demands. Xerox's reprographic manufacturing operation was able to work with marketing in addressing the areas of spare parts required in the field. By reducing lead times on these parts Xerox was better able to meet customer demand. As Pierre Landry said, "When a customer wants toner, or a copier fixed, they don't want to wait."

DISTRIBUTION RESOURCE PLANNING

Another area of marketing that becomes more active in a Just-in-Time environment is dealing with a company's distribution centers. In a manufacturing company that supplies finished goods to its distribution centers, a continual problem is how to integrate manufacturing and distribution on a Just-in-Time basis. Since most distribution systems are based on the order point method (when the inventory at the distribution center is depleted to a certain level it is replenished from the supply at the central facility), when it comes time to reorder from the factory the demands from the distribution centers tend to be "surprises." Like APCOM's problem with their customer, manufacturing doesn't have visibility into the specific needs of the distribution network.

The way to solve this dilemma is through Distribution Resource Planning (DRP). DRP provides the necessary interface between the material plans at the factory and the needs of the distribution centers to satisfy marketing. This is accomplished by taking the overall manufacturing plan and integrating the branch warehouse requirements at the master schedule level. The results provided are the time-phased requirements for each distribution center and for each individual item. The master scheduler can then schedule the factory to meet the needs of the distribution network, rather than assuming average rates of usage that can be significantly in error.

By using DRP, not only is the distribution inventory properly located, but it is also in the proper quantities for good customer service. The distribution centers can have the items they need on hand as opposed either to running the factory well but starving the customers or to meeting the customer's needs at the expense of running the factory poorly.

MARKETING AND DESIGN ENGINEERING

In an effort to meet their customers' needs, many Just-in-Time companies are bringing marketing into the product design phases, so the items produced are not only manufacturable, they also can be sold. As Bently Nevada's Joe Shull explains it, ''Product development is not a relay race. Somebody doesn't go out and develop a product and then hand it over to the marketing organization and say, 'here's our product, now go sell it.' It goes down a lot easier if you've gotten sales and marketing people involved from the outset.''

Although many companies have trimmed the variety of options they offer customers to reduce the proliferation of components, taking good care of what your customers want remains paramount. Black and Decker's Ed Parrish said, ''We don't want to compete with plain vanilla.'' In other words, they want to be able to offer their customers a choice of products. How many options does a company offer, and how much trade-off time does a company offer for that option selection ability while not sacrificing their Just-in-Time production? Bently Nevada's Shull thinks ''marketing and sales are the best qualified to answer those questions of where to meet the customer and what kind of lead times we need to be competitive.'' The key, as in all Just-in-Time operations is communication and cooperation. It's doing business as a group effort, rather than a series of solo efforts.

HELPING THE CUSTOMER UNDERSTAND JUST-IN-TIME

Part of selling Just-in-Time to the customer is to really work with them to establish their needs as well as to begin to educate them in the process of Just-in-Time. A Just-in-Time vendor's marketing organization needs to make sure the customer understands why smaller order quantities benefit everybody. They need to tell the customer about the pilot projects they have going on in the factory, explaining how the company is approaching manufacturing. This means sharing information with enthusiasm and selling the customer on the advantages of the supplier's ability to produce just in time.

If a customer has been ordering once a month, a supplier will be doing them a favor by letting them know the advantages of weekly or daily deliveries, especially as regards to inventory storage and incoming inspection. By delivering quality products more frequently in smaller quantities a customer would be receiving them as he would be using them, with the potential for greater responsiveness and a lower cost.

This is not an overnight process. APCOM had to work with one of their customers for over a year, proving they could do what they said before the customer would listen. As Don Rice points out, "In doing so, we established a very strong relationship. Then we told them, 'now that you see what we can do, we'd like to enhance that even more,' and we showed them the benefits they could really get. By relying on past performance, they knew that if we said we could do this we would do it. It takes quite a bit of time to convince them, but performance is the important aspect here."

JUST-IN-TIME—MAKING MARKETING'S JOB EASIER

Performance, of course, is the true test of promises in manufacturing, and in this regard Just-in-Time manufacturing has been excellent news for marketing. By improving quality, and reducing order quantities, companies like Tektronix have been able to offer their marketing departments a substantial flexibility and responsiveness to lead times. At Tek it used to be that customer demands required a month's lead time. They have now lowered that to ship in as little as two days.

A company's ability to be responsive to the needs of the marketplace with a relatively short lead time is an essential competitive ingredient. It is also one of the primary benefits a Just-in-Time operation can offer a customer. This ability truly allows marketing to do its job of working with the customer, seeing to their changing demands while continuing to deliver a quality product on time and with lowered costs. This has been a real selling point for many Just-in-Time suppliers. APCOM recently picked up another large customer because of this ability.

"What we can offer," says APCOM's Rice, "is competent delivery of a quality product. When we say it's going to be there, it will be there. That's what our customer found out. Not only do we offer that, but we can also provide them the resources to eliminate redundant inventory. Just-in-Time was a selling point. It was interesting to watch their middle management respond to this. Their upper management came in, and we sold them. When it came down to execution, their middle management began talking about the sales job we had put over on them." They didn't believe APCOM could live up to their claims. Of course APCOM's ability to perform as promised won them over.

Prior to establishing this relationship, APCOM's customer had a person whose job title was expediter. Each week purchasing would supply her with a list of things that were supposed to arrive. Her time was then spent calling each vendor and asking if they were going to be shipping on time, and what they were not going to ship. According to Rice, "We let them do that for about a month, and then our VP of marketing called up and said, 'we've been dealing with you for a month; have you noticed anything not being shipped on time?' ('No.') 'Would it matter if I told you we were always going to ship on time?' ('Yes.') 'That's what our intentions are, and we promise that if we ever think we're going to miss something, we'll call you first, before you call us.' This was a little different response than she was used to getting from a vendor," added Rice. "We haven't had to call yet."

As Bently Nevada's Joe Shull said, "Just-in-Time has to be negotiated on a sales level with each customer, and the customer has to be sold on the idea that this is going to benefit him. Ultimately you're doing this for the customer."

What Just-in-Time does is help the marketing department turn manufacturing into a competitive weapon. When a company can say, "Our manufacturing process is high performance. It's fast track. It's short lead times, on time delivery, and low cost," then as Joe Shull believes, "You'll be the only one in your business out there."

Though APCOM's water heater element market is highly specialized, they have demonstrated Shull's belief. As Rice said, "our competitors cannot provide the same things that we can. The reasons other companies go to our competitors are primarily regional reasons. We offer an equal or better product than our competition, at an equal or better price, but with much better delivery." As proof of their point, APCOM now has only one other competitor in the United States. The rest have left the field since APCOM got its act together.

For many companies the competition is very stiff and coming at them from every angle. In these environments Just-in-Time has been a real motivating factor for marketing. This has been particularly true when a company has a lot of competition from off-shore. But as Bently Nevada's Joe Shull illustrates, "There is actually no way that a Japanese manufacturer can compete with an American manufacturer. They have too many strikes against them. They have to import all their raw materials from 3000 miles away, and then they have to ship the finished product 3000 miles back. The cost is too great; the only advantage they have is in the manufacturing process." Shull contends that if an American manufacturer implemented the same type of process, "there is no way a Japanese manufacturer could build for less than an American company. If you can make marketing and salespeople understand that, they'll understand how Just-in-Time can be a competitive weapon."

Xerox's Pierre Landry believes Shull's comments pertain to their off-shore competition as well. "If we can make a quality product where the quality is equal to theirs," says Landry, "and we can match their manufacturing costs, then (competition) becomes an issue of who does the best advertising. Once the word gets to the customer, it's all over. The problem is on the commodities and products the Japanese have attacked; they are still superior in quality, and superior in costs."

SUMMARY

Just-in-Time is an effective way for American manufacturing to fight back and regain the competitive edge. It's marketing's job to get the word out. Just-in-Time has shown itself to be a mighty weapon in attacking the excess in manufacturing. It can now also be a powerful tool in attracting new market shares. What more could a marketing person ask for than high value and low cost?

Chapter 12

Software

The conventional wisdom says, "It's hard to get good help." This may seem especially true as a company begins searching for the right software package to run their factory. Finally, the right system is found, all the bugs are worked out, and the computer is chipping away at the workload. Then along comes a new kid on the block, Just-in-Time. Suddenly, it seems that the good help now in place is going to be no help at all. Fear not. According to the companies with whom we spoke, Just-in-Time has not had a devastating effect on their software packages. However, as companies improve with Just-in-Time, certain features become critical to make sure the software remains a tool that supports what is happening in the plant.

If a company is happy with their existing software, it might not be necessary to throw it out to accommodate these features brought on by Just-in-Time. Most of them can be made by in-house computer programmers.

Even though most companies have found there are not a lot of alterations to be made, a company operating Just-in-Time with standard Manufacturing Resource Planning software should be aware of the new system requirements. The changes that do need to be made fall basically into two categories: those that are absolutely essential—the must-haves, and those that could be beneficial but aren't essential—the nice-to-haves.

MUST-HAVES

DAILY OR SMALLER TIME PERIODS

Some Manufacturing Resource Planning systems divide their basic planning of master scheduling and material requirements planning into weekly time periods, or buckets. Companies like Cummins UK and Hewlett-Packard have cited one of the most important changes they've had to make because of reduced lead times and more frequent deliveries has been the need to accommodate daily or shorter time periods for scheduling. Even though the predominate architecture of today's systems is a plan by date, bucketless approach, which does allow for planning in these daily or smaller periods, some of the older software may need to be reworked to meet these greater planning needs.

This is the one area that possibly could mean a company will need new software. The reason for this is that if you take a bucketed system and try to go to daily buckets, it tends to use up so much disk storage and so much CPU processing power that it can virtually eat up your computer capabilities. Modifying a bucketed software package to plan by date is a do-able but sizable project. Therefore, if there are other reasons for changing software, a company might be better off changing software packages rather than trying to modify their existing package.

Frequent Replanning

As the precision of planning and scheduling increases with Just-in-Time, so does the need for frequent replanning. When you're planning in terms of days, it becomes more important to be able to replan on a daily basis. For most companies, this means net change replanning. Preceding their involvement with Just-in-Time, Black and Decker was one of the pioneers in net change replanning. Net change replans only the items that have changed since the last replanning run. Regeneration is the other type of planning, and this approach replans everything regardless of whether or not there has been a change.

Net change replanning can be run on a daily basis more economically and more practically than regeneration. Less work needs to be done by the computer, and the results are easier to interpret, since they are only the items that have changed. With a frequent regeneration, it's not obvious what's changed and what's the same as yesterday.

Most Manufacturing Resource Planning software is net change, and has been for some years now. However, if your software is not net change, and if you find it impractical to do daily regenerations and use them effectively, you may need to consider upgrading your software. While it would be possible to modify your software from regeneration to net change, this is not typically done. Instead, the planning module is typically replaced with newer software.

Reducing the lead times to make and buy components produces many benefits, one of which is less rescheduling. Whenever components can be made or bought in days rather than weeks, there will be a dramatic reduction in action messages—rescheduling in and/or rescheduling out. The volume of these types of changes are directly related to time. The greater the time, the greater the number of forecast errors and customer changes.

SIMPLIFIED REPORTING OF PRODUCTION ACTIVITY
As order quantities get smaller and more frequent, it becomes increasingly more costly to keep track of what's on order and what's working in the shop. The objective of these simplified handling activities is, first, to reduce the cost of tracking smaller and more frequent orders, and, second, to ease the reporting of items on the factory floor in a way that doesn't impede a company's ability to work with small order quantities.

If a company is not doing operation-to-operation tracking or is not issuing dispatch lists to the shop floor, the software must be able to provide a simplified way for tracking the work-in-process. Whichever method a company chooses, whether issuing simplified work orders, firm planned orders, or no work orders at all, the software will need to be modified to support the system.

Another necessary software component in this area is the capability to handle post-deduct inventory transaction processing. As mentioned earlier, post-deduct, or "backflushing," is the process of reducing inventory records after the product has been built. This is feasible when the bills of material are accurate, product build times are relatively short, all substitution and scrap are separately and properly documented or when intermediate deduct points are used along the line.

Many of today's software packages already contain a post-deduct capability, but they may not include the option to set post-deduct points by operation, as opposed to after a product has been completed. Some companies will be able to use the system without set post-deduct points, and others will have to modify their systems to include this capability.

MULTIPLE INVENTORY LOCATIONS
As companies move to implementing a Just-in-Time environment, more and more of them have turned to point-of-use inventory storage, lo-

cated in various areas around the shop floor. Like the inventory contained in restricted store areas, the accuracy of point-of-use inventory must also be maintained. Consequently, the software must be able to account for these multiple inventory locations. It also should be able to tie those locations into the post-deduct areas as previously discussed.

VENDOR SCHEDULING

We examined in Chapter 10 the impact vendor scheduling has had on a supplier's capacity to deliver Just-in-Time. In terms of software, as with in-house scheduling, daily or hourly time buckets are also needed to bring material into the plant as needed. We also mentioned the highly successful link between Tachikawa and Nissan, who plan in increments of three hours. It is important to note that most software on the market today does not address vendor scheduling, but it is fairly simple to write in-house. The majority of Manufacturing Resource Planning software does contain the ability to maintain purchasing and vendor-related data. The programming task, therefore, becomes one of primarily "retrieval and display" programming, which is typically less difficult than starting from scratch.

Smaller time periods, frequent replanning, simplified handling of smaller order quantities, multiple inventory locations, and vendor schedules are the most important changes or modifications the companies we spoke with made to their existing Manufacturing Resource Planning system software. For the most part, the basis for many of these changes is already contained in the majority of standard packages. By applying these modifications, most Manufacturing Resource Planning software will work for all kinds of Just-in-Time manufacturing, whether we're talking about *flow industries* or *repetitive* manufacturing or the typical intermittent production shop.

THE NICE-TOS

The three issues addressed here are capabilities that many companies would probably find are nice to have as part of their software. They are not absolutely essential to running Just-in-Time.

RATE-BASED PLANNING GENERATOR

As Just-in-Time moves even make-to-order companies toward a more repetitive fashion of manufacturing, there is a growing need for the software to have a rate-based planning generator. In a repetitive environment, schedules can be set according to daily output rates. If a company needs ten of a particular item everyday for the next year, a rate-based planning generator would simply make those hundreds of transactions automatically. Black and Decker has found this to be a real time-saver in their process. The software also should be able to generate and maintain these repetitive schedules, while being able to avoid discrete order maintenance.

RESPONSIVENESS—ON-LINE INTERACTIVE AND FLEXIBLE SOFTWARE

The software should be on line, interactive, and flexible. This means it should have the ability to be updated with at least daily schedule updates. This kind of flexibility is important to allow for continuous change. It must offer a simulation of reality, representing what is really going on in the facility. If a company is scheduling in terms of days, the software must reflect that. If the company changes their system to scheduling in hourly increments, the system must be able to adjust to those changes.

Again, the point here is for a company to see how their standard package meets these particular needs and to modify those places it does not. Hopefully, in the future, these needs will be properly addressed in the standard packages themselves. Until that time, these changes can be made in-house.

ELECTRONIC DATA EXCHANGE

As demonstrated by both Xerox and Nissan/Tachikawa, as more and more companies begin communicating via electronic data interfaces, the software will need to be able to make these telecommunication linkups, and facilitate the transactions in this manner. This is one area that technology is changing very rapidly, with new and better telecommunication systems coming on-line daily. Effective telecommunications capabilities means that software between users must be compatible and easy to use. This will allow schedules and changes to be communicated rapidly to suppliers. This capability will also help reduce the large amount of time spent making these changes over the telephone or through the mail. It will let companies feed directly into each other's scheduling systems, cutting waste and improving efficiency.

Xerox has shown that by tying together their Manufacturing Resource Planning system to their supplier's Manufacturing Resource Planning system, Xerox's planned order releases take the place of forecasting by the supplier. This interface provides the supplier with the ability to know exactly what Xerox anticipates it is going to need from them. It also allows Xerox to know this need has been communicated and acted upon. The time saved, through better communication with the vendor and through ease of scheduling, is tremendous. We will see more of this in the years to come as companies begin to work on improving their electronic communications.

SUMMARY

The Just-in-Time changes affecting system software are not severe. Most of the needs already exist in some form in existing packages. The point here is that with some modification, companies can update their existing software programs to address the specific needs of Just-in-Time.

In the next chapter we will see some of the practical applications of these system calculations and measurements and how they impact a company's accounting systems. As Just-in-Time attacks the wasteful manufacturing practices of a company, one of the places that has felt the greatest fallout has been accounting. We will look into some of the ways companies have successfully met these concerns of measuring overhead and lessened the deluge of paper that has threatened to bury accounting departments beneath reams of daily invoices and purchase orders.

Chapter 13

Measurements—
Accounting for Just-in-Time

"NEW MEASUREMENT SYSTEMS MUST REFLECT THE STRATEGY, TECHNOLOGY, PRODUCT MIX AND MARKETS OF A FIRM."

We have spent the greater part of twelve chapters diagraming the impact of Just-in-Time on the traditional manufacturing system. Now it is time to see how companies are accounting for these changes. There are two areas that must be examined: (1) how Just-in-Time has affected the department which must bear the brunt of responsibility for gathering and measuring the performance of the total business; accounting; (2) how companies are handling the manufacturing operational measurements.

FINANCIAL MEASUREMENTS

There have been some reported cases where implementing Just-in-Time has turned an accountant's desk into something resembling a paper Mt. Everest. Daily receipts and invoices pour in from shipping and receiving and then drift into teetering piles, which even the stoutest of sherpa guides would find too treacherous to traverse. This, of course, does not have to be the only way to the top of the Just-in-Time mountain.

In order to measure properly the fruits of Just-in-Time labor, we must first understand the impact Just-in-Time is going to have on the measurement systems. This means addressing the traditional notions of overhead absorption, altering the way in which accounting departments collect their cost data, and making sure the accounting department is not overwhelmed by paperwork. The process for attacking these elements is the same as the attack on other areas impacted by Just-in-Time. In this case, involve the accountants early.

165

Bently Nevada's Ray Bacon began working with his cost accountant from the beginning to try and relieve some of the shock to the system. They had to figure out together how they could address these traditional concerns in a manner that made sense in this new operating mode. "The stumbling blocks we've encountered," says Bacon's accounting associate, John Stephans, "haven't been that great. The key is communication. You've got one guy in manufacturing thinking one thing, and another in finance thinking something else. You've got to realize that (as an accountant) you can't always look at where you've been, but where you're going. If you play as a team, you're not going to have problems."

It is essential that everyone affected by Just-in-Time understand the "whys" behind the process. If manufacturing were to set up daily deliveries with a vendor and not include accounting in the process, trouble is going to quickly erupt. Hewlett-Packard's Charlene Adair has seen a number of Just-in-Time implementation programs completely stopped because accounting was not brought in on the changes. As Bently Nevada's Stephans explains, "Some of the things Bacon presents to me are 180 degrees from what we've been doing. You've got to understand, manufacturing is a little faster paced than the accounting profession. Just-in-Time is leading to a different way of manufacturing parts. Once they went through a number of different work centers and stages, but what happens if one center has everything right there." What Stephans is saying is that new ways have to be found to deal with accounting for overhead absorption and direct labor.

The history of modern accounting practices is really anything but contemporary. Today's practices are based, in most part, on systems developed in the early years of the twentieth century. They have evolved but in principle have remained true to the character of the manufacturing environment from which they sprang. According to Dr. Robert S. Kaplan, former Dean of the Business School at Carnegie Mellon University, they were developed for mass production of a few standardized items with a high direct-labor content. "The goal of those companies," Kaplan said in an interview in *Corporate Accounting*, "was to watch their direct-labor costs very closely—and their accounting systems reflected that. They measured direct-labor time and dollars accurately. Seventy years ago, overhead might only have been $0.50 to $0.60 for every direct-labor dollar. Rather than having an elaborate system to track the overhead dollars, we have developed systems that allocate the overhead to products based on what was the highest value-added operation—direct labor.''

Today, with overhead often running as high as 20 times that of direct labor dollars, accounting has never gone back to rethink the measures and principles adopted years ago for an entirely different environment.

One of the basic principles of Just-in-Time, the production rate equaling the demand (sales) rate, is not always compatible with this process of measurement. Most companies avoid expensing overhead costs as they are incurred by absorbing them into inventory. The rate of absorption is often tied to direct labor hours. As an example, for every direct labor hour produced, $5 to $10 in overhead or burden costs are absorbed into inventory. Under this approach, unfavorable variances occur when the actual overhead costs for the accounting period are underabsorbed, that is, not covered by inventory produced. The result is a reduction in profit. Favorable variances occur when the actual overhead costs for the accounting period are overabsorbed. In this case, by overproducing, profits are increased. Actual costs, though, remain the same.

Unfortunately, overabsorbing expenses in this fashion sometimes acts as a tempting variable to create short-term paper profits. Increasing production rates to overabsorb fixed expenses builds inventory, while increasing these short-term profits. This ploy is known as ''JFI or Just-For-Income'' inventory. It is also the antithesis of Just-in-Time manufacturing.

Though few companies would openly admit to producing JFI inventory, the process of reconciling overhead with direct labor continues. Again, the question we must ask is, Why? To get closer to answering this it is important to briefly explain how cost is measured.

FIGURING COST

There are basically two types of cost accounting systems, *job order* and *process costing*. ''Cost'' is a rather slippery term in accounting. It can be used to represent a variety of different ideas. Therefore, it should be preceded by a modifier to properly direct its meaning. Full cost, for example, means all the resources used for a cost objective. In some circumstances this can be easily measured. If you pay $30 for a pair of shoes, your price is, obviously, $30.

Suppose, though, the question becomes, What is the full cost of manufacturing that pair of shoes? A shoe factory may make thousands of shoes a month. Some may be wing-tips, while others are oxfords or loafers. They may be made of either leather or a synthetic material, and sizes and widths may vary from tiny to extra large. Needless to say, the costs are going to be as different for each pair of shoes as the number of sizes and styles.

Full cost is then defined as the the sum of the direct costs, the materials and labor, and a fair share of the indirect costs, the services which are not adding value to the product. The problem, of course, arises in trying to allocate the indirect costs. It's easy to account for the leather in the shoes and the labor it took to make them, but where in all of this is the salary of the factory superintendent, or the designer, or the accountant who is trying to measure the whole process. The difficulty comes in trying to trace this cost to the object made.

Job order costing collects cost for each physical identifiable job or batch of work as it moves through the factory regardless of the accounting period in which the work is done. Process costing collects cost for all the products worked on during an accounting period and determines the unit costs by dividing the total costs by the total number of units on which have been worked.

This returns us to the problem of overhead absorption. As the cost of direct labor becomes a decreasing amount of the manufacturing cost, and the indirect an increasing part, how does a company reconcile their overhead costs? An excellent example (albeit slightly tongue-in-cheek) of this problem of figuring indirect and direct labor costs and their relationship to overhead is illustrated by what the Quaker Oats company might experience. In their process of making puffed rice, all the direct labor involved is one operator pulling the trigger on the cannon. It takes half a second to pull the trigger, but there is still considerable overhead. If Quaker Oats were to try to amortize their overhead against the labor, they would end up with a situation that a few seconds could cost a million dollars.

What this suggests is the idea that high costs are associated with labor. The answer would then be to cut the labor force. If the labor force is reduced by 50 percent, then we should be cutting the overhead by 50 percent. This, of course, is not true—the overhead remains the same.

With Just-in-Time this problem becomes an even greater concern when confronted with variable order quantities. Accounting must figure out how to allocate setup costs when the quantity varies. Part of the answer is to reduce setups, so that the costs for these procedures become insignificant. As mentioned in Chapter 5, Black and Decker does this by making setups a variance.

The problem of accounting for direct labor remains though as we introduce cellular manufacturing. What companies are discovering is that as the product moves through the cell, there's no real need to collect cost for each operation. Many companies are turning toward a process costing approach, and merely reporting how much time was spent in the cell against how many pieces have come out the other end, and not worrying about the loss of precision in accounting. All costs, not just direct labor, are then assigned to the cell.

Since Just-in-Time requires less sophistication from a cost accounting point of view, the closer a manufacturer moves to Just-in-Time on the factory floor, the closer he is to adopting process costing. This helps eliminate the problems often associated with overhead absorption, and allows for productivity to be based on the total number of employees and not just direct labor. This to some degree is what a number of companies are trying to do when they say they are treating all labor as indirect. They are then calculating their overhead against the total job rather than just one element.

Another consideration is to examine costs over the life of a given project, rather than from a monthly, quarterly, or annual percentage. As the cumulative effect of quality, inventory reduction, and the reduction of cycle times and lead times sets in, the financial performance measures may show a marked improvement. In the short-term, though, these effects might not be able to be measured. In order to accommodate this protracted period, it would mean that new concepts of *project accounting* would need to be devised.

"New measurement systems," says Dr. Kaplan, "must reflect the strategy, technology, product mix, and markets of a firm. This requires accountants to play an expanded role in understanding and monitoring the firm's critical success parameters and in continually modifying their measurement systems as the strategies and technologies change within the firm."

This process change will invariably require accounting to become more innovative in how they go about the collection of their data. This may actually mean that accountants, like design engineers, will have to come out of their offices and go out onto the factory floor, or into the marketing department, or the research and development departments.

As in implementing other Just-in-Time methods, accounting departments need not be completely revamped. The process should begin with a pilot program, starting small and building on success. As Kaplan suggests, this may mean isolating a certain part of the factory, in a financial sense, and then attempting to try new forms of accounting under those circumstances.

As production methods change, performance measurements to standards also will be simplified. Just as production people strive to motivate workers, improve quality, and reduce inventory, accountants will have to strive to measure the performance along these new dimensions. Because Just-in-Time brings changes to operators' responsibilities coupled with changes in how they are measured, the new emphasis in accounting must be on total costs for the process, lumping together direct labor, indirect labor, and staff contributions. The traditional methods of setting standards, comparing actual labor against them, and spreading overhead by department is no longer viewed as the best method of cost accounting.

As we mentioned earlier, as many operations and stocking points cease to exist data collection should become easier. There will also be fewer inventory transactions about which to worry, thus making it easier to obtain financial control of the inventory. "The biggest single change that we have seen in accounting," says Omark's Vern Pearson, "is that we no longer talk about standard costs of a manufacturing operation. We talk about actual costs with everything getting lumped together. We have departments that used to report twenty operations. Now, they report one. We just don't need as much detail." And as Pearson continues, "what the cost accountants have done is stay current with the production operation. If we were fighting them, we would be unable to make these things happen."

Another Just-in-Time activity that has aided the accounting process has been the standardization of containers. By moving to this like kind of material containerization, accounting will find that the efforts of reporting and counting work-in-process have been greatly streamlined. It's simply easier to access stock when everything is in a standardized format.

RAISING THE CAUTION FLAG

There are accounting caution signs a company should be aware of as they begin the implementation of Just-in-Time. Because of the previous practice of producing more than is being sold, as a hedge against overhead variances and the calculation of profit, a company could actually show a loss of profit as Just-in-Time takes hold. These negative variances need to be addressed when a company begins planning for the coming year. Since Just-in-Time may be cranking down the production rate, a company might not be producing at the rate established to cover overhead, and unfavorable variances will arise. This might be in spite of the fact that sales rates are being met. The measurement system needed under these circumstances is one based on whether or not the company meets its total output.

BEWARE OF OVERWHELMING ACCOUNTING WITH PAPERWORK

As discussed in Chapter 10, Just-in-Time has a profound impact on suppliers and accounts payable. Hewlett-Packard accountants found themselves particularly hard hit by the increase in paperwork brought on by daily deliveries. They handled the problem through their system software, streamlining their process through bar coding, and vendor agreements. All transactions throughout the company should be viewed as non-value adding activities. The spirit of Just-in-Time is to eliminate them wherever possible and to simplify them if they are needed.

When a firm has worked under the traditional process of a separate order for every delivery, accompanied by a separate invoice and a separate check, it won't take long after initiating Just-in-Time that the accounting department will find itself thoroughly inundated with paperwork. From an internal control standpoint, the process is difficult to change. There is always the feeling that if you don't have a purchase order authorizing material delivery, vendors could take advantage of the system. Control does not mean paperwork, but rather procedures, authorizations, and audits, and these can be done with frequent deliveries. They do not require a purchase order for every delivery.

How then does a Just-in-Time customer pay its supplier without these controls? Xerox's Pierre Landry suggests that by building trust through Just-in-Time, and then utilizing the capabilities of linked electronic systems, that invoicing might actually become obsolete. He believes that a company like Xerox should eventually be able to figure, "If we completed a copier and shipped it out today, we must have used (our vendors) parts. So, every month, I'll figure out how many copiers I've shipped (or have in process) and since obviously his parts must be in the copier, then we'll electronically transfer funds to him for that number of parts. This is what Just-in-Time is all about, the elimination of waste."

Getting the accounting departments to move in these directions may be easier in some companies than others. The Tennant Company was also deluged by the invoicing process and diligently brought their accountants into the process, exposing them to many of the things they were trying to do to help facilitate their change. The biggest problem for them, though, was not their accountants, but outside auditors who were now confronted with the problem of cellular processes that no longer accounted for every operation.

SUPPORTING STRATEGY

The essential need is "to devise a system that is supportive of and consistent with the firm's overall strategy," says Harvard's Dr. Kaplan. At the same time, he makes it clear that accountants don't set strategy, senior operating executives do. What accountants can do is understand the strategy and then devise the measurement system to fit.

With manufacturing execution systems being revisited and challenged by Just-in-Time and with significant improvements in the management of material flow, few stones have been left unturned. The impact on accounting procedures has been great, but like those visited on Manufacturing Resource Planning systems, they have been mainly for the good. As operations are reduced, setups made easier and more efficient, with fewer stocking points and flatter bills of material, sophisticated cost systems also can be significantly simplified. How this is accomplished is up to the people involved.

OPERATIONAL MEASUREMENTS

Measuring the performance of manufacturing is not only a matter of dollars and hours spent. How a company addresses their progress in the areas of Just-in-Time is also a significant issue. Setting objectives and goals is an individual standard established by each company. But there are some new performance standards that Just-in-Time has brought on board.

Just-in-Time's need for valid schedules is actually one way to reconfirm valid performance. The results of a company operating with valid schedules will be reflected by its on-time completion rate. Since producing more than a company needs to is as bad under Just-in-Time as producing less than one needs, performance measurements must be based on whether or not a company is meeting their schedule.

Another measurement companies will need to establish is one that charts the progress of the various areas of Just-in-Time. This will invariably mean a new measurement for lead time reductions. In the past the priority for changes in lead times were primarily associated with runtime. The other aspects that affected lead times such as queues, setup, and move time were not given the same importance. Since Just-in-Time has attacked all those areas, their cumulative impact on lead times has been significant and that must also be measured as an important company yardstick.

Many companies are also able to chart their progress by examining their increase in inventory turnovers, as well as their responsiveness to the marketplace. Both of these are prime indicators of the progress of Just-in-Time.

The important point is that the results gained from trying to account for Just-in-Time using the standards of old probably won't add up. What companies must realize is that Just-in-Time has changed the standards of performance, so new ways of measuring them must also be created.

THE FRUSTRATION INDEX

Even though accounting for performance and costs are at the heart of any measurement system, there is still one key measurement that a company won't need an accountant to perform. It's known as *the frustration index*. This is a people measurement. It reflects the level of frustration within the company. When the frustration level is high, it means things are not going well. People are upset. Expediting and firefighting bring with them fingerpointing and complaining. No one enjoys working in this kind of environment. Worse, yet, instead of directing their energies to correcting the problem, people direct their attention and efforts to making excuses. This is nothing but waste, going completely against the objectives of Just-in-Time.

What a company will discover as it starts to produce valid schedules, improve its quality, and make Just-in-Time a reality, the frustration index goes down. Though we offer this as our final thought on measurements, it might serve a company about to implement Just-in-Time best by making it the first measurement. When a company does this honestly, without smoke screens and mirrors, Just-in-Time will help eliminate much of the frustration, and measure up to its advance notice.

Chapter 14

The Continually Improving Process

We have stated throughout this book that no matter how good a manufacturing company is, it can always become better. It is only by actively taking the steps to meet this bold challenge that American manufacturing can hope to reassert its leadership in the world marketplace. Just-in-Time has offered companies an approach to meet this goal by providing a total manufacturing fitness program. It has effectively integrated and focused all the ingredients of the manufacturing process into a recipe that both nourishes the system and trims the waste. Just-in-Time has proved to be an effective catalyst for companies to break down the lethargy of *business as usual*, allowing them to exercise all the muscle and brain power of their organization into a world-class operation.

We have outlined in these pages what the process is today. Like all such methodologies as companies begin to travel the Just-in-Time course, modifications will continue to improve the path to greater manufacturing productivity. What we have tried to provide is a structure, based on simplicity and common sense. The objectives are also straightforward: to eliminate waste and add value. In many companies these techniques may already be in place, needing only the focusing mechanism that Just-in-Time offers to properly engage them. Others may be new and profound changes that could cause a company to rethink the priorities they have pursued in the past. Whatever their primary effect, these Just-in-Time concepts can only help. As Black and Decker's Ken Good said earlier, "It's hard to make a case against Just-in-Time." And as most would agree, why would someone want to?

As we have shown, Just-in-Time is the continual challenge of the process. From its teamwork concepts—bringing together all the people involved in the company process; honoring their authority, while building an environment open to change; establishing trust and opening communication, generating intensity, enthusiasm, and a sense of mission—to its practical plant aspects—multi-skilled operators, quality at the source, scrap rates measured in parts per million, the reduction of inventories, lead times, order quantities and setup times—to the necessity of valid schedules—allowing a company to know exactly what it needs and when—this is Just-in-Time.

It is an approach designed to increase productivity and profits. Just-in-Time goes down to the deep, inner fibers of a manufacturing company's strength and weakness, toning them into a powerful performer. As with any process of getting in shape, the effects are not seen quickly. Change is gradual, even though the pain of exercising long-neglected muscles may be felt immediately. Pain in this context is good. It is a positive indication that the procedures for finding problems are working. The more those tight, once-ignored areas are flexed the stronger and more effective they become.

We have seen by practical illustration the benefits that come from these manufacturing body-building exercises: being able to reduce floor space, eliminate receiving inspection, collapse routings, flatten bills of materials and join operations in a cellular fashion.

We have outlined how to improve vendor relations, by providing trust, continuity, and consistency. We have demonstrated the importance of vendor scheduling, giving suppliers the visibility necessary to deliver Just-in-Time. We have also explained the advantages of reducing a company's vendor base to better establish a true win-win atmosphere between customer and supplier—the result being reliable deliveries, excellent quality, and reduced costs.

Just-in-Time has offered companies the means to simplify their processes from design through production. Through the cooperation of engineers, operators, and management, products can be better designed to make the manufacturing process easier. By moving to mixed model schedules, a company can provide the flexibility necessary to meet the needs of their customer, lowering lead times, while building only what is needed. By lowering order quantities, improving quality, flattening the bill of material, and reducing queues, companies have been able to move more efficiently material via the demand pull system. This has not only simplified the way product travels through the line, and helped reduce material handling, but it has also aided in the elimination of work orders. Companies have also begun using standardized containers to facilitate both the production and measurement processes.

Through the integration of all these Just-in-Time aspects a company can meet the initial objectives: to increase productivity, lower costs, improve quality and have the production rate equal the sales rate. But even that is not the end, because things can still be better: Productivity can be increased further, obsolescence can be reduced, engineering can provide even more manufacturable designs, improving quality is a constant drive toward zero defects, and lead times can be continually shortened. Maintaining a company's fitness is not a goal, it is a full-time commitment. Just-in-Time offers the banner, the motivation, and the tools to keep this going. It is hard work, but it is rewarding work for everybody involved.

How can a company make certain that it is on the right path? One answer is the Just-in-Time checklist assembled by Tektronix's Ralph Todd. (See Figure 14-1.) It is important to realize, though, that every company needs to look at their environment and situation to see how this checklist fits. For example, demand rate may not equal the production rate, but that may be all right for your company. One hundred percent completion to customer service order dates may not be possible, but that should be the goal. Please remember that this is a guideline, and all of it will not apply to every company.

Data Integrity   Y   N

1. Inventory record accuracy 95% or better.   ☐   ☐
   Stockrooms and point-of-use storage.   ☐   ☐

2. Bill of material accuracy 99% or better.   ☐   ☐
   For cost need and post-deduct of inventory.   ☐   ☐
   Bill of material flattened.   ☐   ☐

3. Routing accuracy maintained by line flow.   ☐   ☐
   Defined engineering standards for costing.   ☐   ☐
   Manufacturing process adhered to.   ☐   ☐

Education

4. All operators are trained in overall Just-in-Time practices.   ☐   ☐

5. Individual operators are cross-trained, take self-initiative
   to move to point of need, and have authority to stop the line.   ☐   ☐

6. Management support for the Thinking Worker.   ☐   ☐

Figure 14-1. Tektronix's Just-in-Time Checklist

	Y	N
7. All functional organizations (engineering, purchasing, marketing, and manufacturing) are part of the problem-resolution team.	□	□

Material Flow

| 8. Weekly or more frequent delivery of 80% of materials to the plant and material delivered to point of use. | □ | □ |
| 9. Parts are only produced as required and built in quantity approaching one. (Object is to keep the material moving on the line, not *keeping* the labor busy if not needed at the next operation.) | □ | □ |

Quality

| 10. All inspection sequences have been eliminated and quality is part of the individual operator responsibility. | □ | □ |
| 11. Quality control departments are replaced with process audit functions. | □ | □ |

Planning

12. Daily rates and level schedule established and met on due date.	□	□
13. Manufacturing Resource Planning system is used for internal planning, customer committing, and vendor schedules and vendor capacity planning.	□	□
14. Management participates in the planning and replanning process and commits to a realistic capacity level.	□	□
15. Customer service 100% as committed, and production equals demand.	□	□

Process Changes

16. Single-digit setups established (less than 10 minutes).	□	□
17. Where feasible, work orders are eliminated or simplified and priorities controlled by demand pull.	□	□
18. Reduction in the number of active vendors/suppliers and they are part of the production planning process.	□	□
19. Simplified manufacturing process to: Provide management by sight vs. complex control systems. Identify and surface problems with immediate resolution.	□ □	□ □
20. Accounting systems are redesigned to operate a Just-in-Time environment.	□	□
21. Manufacturing is actively involved in the design of product for manufacturability.	□	□

Figure 14-1. Tektronix's Just-in-Time Checklist (continued)

	Y	N
22. Manufacturing engineering is located in the production area and immediately available for problem resolution.	☐	☐
23. Manufacturing processes are adhered to and formal change processes are established.	☐	☐
24. Manufacturing production line has been relayed out to provide mixed model runs and minimum material handling.	☐	☐
25. Compensation for employees is measured on a team contribution basis.	☐	☐

Results

26. Operating results have been achieved in seven of the nine following areas: ☐   ☐
    ☐ Reduced floor space
    ☐ Reduced work-in-process
    ☐ Reduced obsolescence
    ☐ Improved manufacturing process time
    ☐ Increased flexibility to meet fluctuating customer demands
    ☐ Increased productivity
    ☐ Increased quality
    ☐ Reduced cumulative lead times
    ☐ Reduced inventory

Figure 14-1. Tektronix's Just-in-Time Checklist (continued)

Because the Tektronix checklist does not apply to every company, we have set forth what we call our, *"Bill of Doing It Right."* This list offers a company a starting place to begin measuring what Just-in-Time elements a company has incorporated into their process.

The Bill of Doing It Right

1. Authority with the Worker.
   This is the notion of the Thinking Worker, and a reversing of the idea of "I think, you work."
2. The ability to stop the line.
   This is often an essential to eliminate quality problems where they occur.
3. Maintain capacity balance throughout the line, where a line is used.
   A company no longer runs at maximum rate at every location on the line. By using demand pull an item is made when it is authorized.

4. No layoffs for higher productivity.

   If a company is soliciting productivity suggestions from its employees, and then uses them to eliminate jobs, there won't be too many more suggestions coming.

5. Establishing an atmosphere where surfacing problems is socially acceptable.

   This is what Peter Drucker called "effectiveness versus efficiency." In other words a company must have a total dedication to identifying and fixing problems as they surface.

6. Maintaining a total quality program.

   This is a dedication, not a token effort to approach the ideals of "zero defects."

7. Cross-training of operators.

   As companies move to cellular manufacturing, flexible and cross-trained employees become a must.

8. Changing the score card.

   As elements of Just-in-Time come on line a company will need new ways to measure them.

9. Elimination of internal purchase requisitions.

   With paperwork being a waste, working toward the elimination of purchase requisitions simplifies the process even further.

10. A commitment to valid schedules.

    This is essential to know what a company wants and when: eliminating end-of-the-month-crunch, hot lists, expediting, late deliveries, and material shortages.

11. Teamwork.

    Without people working together on the same team Just-in-Time will not be able to make the communication link necessary to integrate the various elements involved.

CONCLUSION

There is no Just-in-Time conclusion, only continual change and improvement. No matter how good a company thinks it is, it can always be better. The Just-in-Time story is still unraveling, but by all accounts it offers the factory of the present the foundation and the tools to provide greater productivity and profit, as well as the opportunity to build a structure able to withstand the competitive pressures of the future.

Sources for Additional Information

Preparing yourself to implement a Class A MRP II system requires careful study of a huge amount of information, far more than could be included in this or any other book. The Oliver Wight Companies can provide further assistance in getting ready, including books on the subject, live education, and reviews of commercially available software packages.

OLIVER WIGHT LIMITED PUBLICATIONS, INC.

Oliver Wight Limited Publications, Inc. was created in 1981 to publish books on planning and scheduling, written by leading educators and consultants in the field.

A complete library of books on Manufacturing Resource Planning, Just-in-Time, and Distribution Resource Planning are available.

For more information, or to order publications, contact:

Oliver Wight Limited Publications, Inc.
5 Oliver Wight Drive
Essex Junction, VT 05452
800-343-0625 or 802-878-8161

OLIVER WIGHT EDUCATION ASSOCIATES

OWEA is made up of a group of independent MRP II educators and consultants aroung the world who share a common philosophy and common goals. Classes directed towards both upper- and middle-level management are being taught in various locations around the U.S. and Canada, as well as abroad. For a detailed class brochure, listing course descriptions, instructors, costs, dates, and locations, or for the name of a recommended consultant in your area, please contact:

Oliver Wight Education Associates
P.O. Box 435
Newbury, NH 03255
800-258-3862 or 603-763-5926

OLIVER WIGHT VIDEO PRODUCTIONS, INC.

The Oliver Wight Video Library offers companies the video-based materials they need to teach the ''critical mass'' of their employees about the principles of MRP II and Just-in-Time. For more information on obtaining the Oliver Wight Video Library, contact:

Oliver Wight Video Productions, Inc.
5 Oliver Wight Drive
Essex Junction, VT 05452
800-343-0625 or 802-878-8161

Glossary

ABC CLASSIFICATION Before computers, practitioners found that if they ranked the inventory items by annual usage in dollars, it would tell them how to best use their scarce resource—manual posting of inventory records. The low-value items were typically put on a simple visual review system of some type to avoid having to make all the necessary inventory entries. With computers, the scarce resource is no longer clerical posting time, but instead the time people would use for planning and controlling. The ABC classification is still used to determine which items should be cycle counted most frequently, which items should have the largest lot sizes, etc.

  The basic principle involves breaking the inventory down into three categories where typically the top 20 percent ranked by annual usage in dollars are called the A items (they will normally account for 80 percent of the dollar activity). The next 30 percent are called the B items, and the next 50 percent are the C items, which usually account for about 5 percent of the annual dollar usage.

AGV Automatic guided vehicle.

ANDON An electronic board that provides visibility of floor status and provides information to help coordinate the efforts of linked work centers. Signal lights are green (running), red (stop), and yellow (needs attention).

ASRS Automatic storage and retrieval system.

BACKFLUSH The deduction from inventory of the component parts used in an assembly or subassembly as they are completed by exploding the bill of material or utilizing a parts list with specific locations that equals the bill by the production count of assemblies produced.

BALANCING OPERATIONS In repetitive Just-in-Time production, trying to match actual output cycle times of all operations to the cycle time of use for parts as required by final assembly, and eventually as required by the market.

BROADCAST SYSTEM   A sequence of specific units to be assembled and completed at a given rate. This sequence is communicated to supply and assembly activities to perform operations and to position material so that it merges with the correct assembled unit.

BUSINESS PLAN   The overall plan for the amount of dollars to be shipped, the amount planned to be in inventory or order backlog, and the amount to be produced. This is the basic business plan in a manufacturing company. The complete business plan would probably also include other planned expenditures such as research and development that are not directly connected with the production functions.

CAD/CAM   The integration of computer aided design and computer aided manufacturing to achieve automation from design through manufacturing.

CAPACITY REQUIREMENTS PLANNING   A time-phased MRP system that not only releases orders, but it also generates planned orders that are used to create lower level material requirements. Capacity requirements plans can be generated then by taking into account the hours by work center by time period needed to produce both the open shop orders and planned shop orders.

CAUSE-AND-EFFECT DIAGRAM   A precise statement of a problem or phenomenon with a branching diagram leading from the statement to the known potential causes. A tool to organize the logic to attack a problem. Also called Ishikawa diagram or fishbone chart.

CELLULAR MANUFACTURING   A manufacturing process that produces families of parts within a single line or cell of machines operated by machinists who work only within the line or cell.

CHANGEOVER   *See* Setup.

CLOSED LOOP MRP   A term used to describe a system built around material requirements planning that also includes production planning, master scheduling, capacity planning, and means for executing the capacity plans such as the input/output report for monitoring it, means for executing the material plans such as the dispatch list and the vendor schedules. Implicit in the concept of a closed loop system is the feedback from the vendors and the shop floor using the input/output report and the anticipated delay reports.

COMPUTER AIDED DESIGN (CAD)   The use of computers in interactive engineering drawing and storage of designs. Programs complete the layout, geometric transformations, projections, rotations, magnifications, and interval (cross-section) views of a part and its relationship with other parts.

COMPUTER AIDED MANUFACTURING (CAM)   Use of computers to program, direct, and control production equipment in the fabrication of manufactured items.

CONTINUOUS FLOW PRODUCTION Lotless production where products flow continuously rather than being proportioned into lots.

CONTROL CHART A statistical device usually used for the study and control of repetitive processes. It is designed to reveal the randomness or trend of deviations from a mean or control value, usually by plotting these. Used to collect data within a process.

CYCLE TIME Time it takes to produce one item; *see* Lead Time.

DEDICATED LINE A production line "permanently" configured to run well-defined parts, one piece at a time from station to station.

DEMAND PULL Usually refers to how material is moved on the factory floor. Demand pull means that materials move only upon request from the next operation. Only when the outbound queue is reduced is the feeding operation authorized to make more. A simple, visible means of queue control in the factory. *See* Push System as the alternative.

DEPENDENT DEMAND Demand on an item is called "dependent" when it can be calculated from the need to manufacture or to replenish inventory for a higher level item. A part that goes into a subassembly has dependent demand. If it is also sold directly to customers as a service part, it has independent demand as well. A raw material that is later converted into semifinished inventory has dependent demand. Demand on the semifinished inventory is likely to be dependent demand unless that semifinished inventory is sold directly to customers. Dependent demand requirements should be calculated using techniques like MRP rather than forecast using order-point techniques.

DISPATCH LIST A schedule for a work center usually generated by computer, usually issued daily, showing the priority sequence of jobs to be done at that work center. Priorities on the dispatch list are kept up to date by the Material Requirements Planning system.

DISTRIBUTION RESOURCE PLANNING (DRP) Material Requirements Planning (MRP) was originally developed as a way to order material to support assembly operations. After it had been in use for a number of years, people began to recognize that distribution inventories also have levels. Branch warehouses draw inventory from a distribution center, which, in turn, replenishes its inventory by ordering in lots from factories. DRP is simply the term given to MRP when it is used to properly time phase these dependent demands on finished goods inventory and plan production at the manufacturing facility to include the distribution system. Just as MRP was extended into areas other than Material Requirements Planning, the same thing happened with DRP. Distribution resource planning includes planning cubage for traffic requirements, converting the distribution requirements plan into dollars, using it for planning manpower requirements at warehouses, and so on.

ECONOMIC ORDER QUANTITY (EOQ)   A type of fixed order quantity that determines the amount of an item to be purchased or manufactured at one time. The intent is to minimize the combined costs of acquiring and carrying inventory. Also called economic lot size or run size.

EOQ1   Reducing setup time and inventory to the point where it is economically sound to produce one piece.

EXCHANGE UNIT   The number of units to be produced before changing the bit, tool, or die.

EXTERNAL SETUP TIME   Elements of a setup procedure performed while the process is in production—that is, while the machine is running.

FINAL-ASSEMBLY SCHEDULE   Plan for what is to be assembled day-by-day.

FIRST-PIECE INSPECTION   A quality check on the first component run after a new setup has been completed.

FISHBONE CHART   *See* Cause-and-Effect Diagram.

FITNESS FOR USE   Involves the quality of a product, but also the appropriateness of its design characteristics as well.

FIVE W'S   Japanese managers ask "why" five times. By the time they receive the answer to the fifth "why," they think they have found the cause of the problem.

FLEXIBLE AUTOMATION   Short setup times and the ability to switch quickly from one product to another.

FLEXIBLE MANUFACTURING SYSTEM   A manufacturing process designed so that the production line may be rebalanced often, rapidly matching output to changes in demand. Involves mixed-model scheduling, multi-skilled operators, standardization of equipment for quick changeover times, and design of the production line to allow workers to do more than one job and to cut down on transportation time between lines.

40/30/30 RULE   Identifies the sources of scrap, rework, and waste as 40 percent product design, 30 percent manufacturing processing, and 30 percent from suppliers.

GROUP TECHNOLOGY   An engineering and manufacturing philosophy that identifies the "sameness" of parts, equipment, or processes. It provides for rapid retrieval of existing designs and anticipates a cellular type production equipment layout.

IMMEDIATE FEEDBACK   The principle of inspecting production as quickly as possible after a part is made and providing information on deviations from desirable output standards so that correction is immediate. Extends to automatic shutdown of a process in case of a defect or a drifting out of desired control range.

INBOUND STOCKPOINT   A defined location next to the place of use on a production flow to which materials are brought as needed and from which material is taken for immediate use. Used with demand pull system.

INDEPENDENT DEMAND   Demand for an inventory item is considered independent when it is unrelated to any higher-level item that the company manufactures or stocks. The demand for a service part that is shipped directly to customers would be considered independent. On the other hand, if that service part were shipped to a branch warehouse, the demand on the service part would be a function of branch warehouse replenishment, and thus would be considered dependent. Generally, independent demand items are those that are carried in finished goods inventories, although not all finished goods items are necessarily independent demand items, because much of their demand might derive from branch warehouses, for example. Independent demand items can be replenished using stock replenishment systems like the order point, although MRP or DRP (if branch warehouses) would give superior results.

INPUT/OUTPUT CONTROL   A simple technique for capacity control where actual output is compared with planned output developed by capacity requirements planning. The input to a work center can be monitored to see if it corresponds with plans so that work centers will not be expected to generate output when material is not available.

INTERNAL SETUP TIME   Elements of a setup procedure performed while the process is not in production.

ISHIKAWA DIAGRAM   *See* Cause-and-Effect Diagram.

JIDOKA   Practice of stopping the production line when a defect occurs.

JUST-IN-TIME   An approach to achieving excellence in a manufacturing company based on continuing elimination of waste and consistent improvement in productivity. Waste is then defined as those things that do not add value to the product.

KANBAN   A method of Just-in-Time production initially developed at Toyota. The Toyota approach uses standard containers with a standard card attached to each. Other companies have found that Kanban cards are not necessary, but rather employ devices such as squares on the floor, ping pong balls, poker chips, etc. It is a pull system in which work centers which use parts signal with a card that they wish to withdraw parts from feeding operations. Kanban in Japanese loosely translated means "card," literally "billboard" or "sign."

LEAD TIME   Total time from when you initiate an activity to when it's completed. For a manufactured product, it includes time for order preparation, receiving, inspection, setup, run time, wait time, move time, and queue time.

LEVEL SCHEDULE   A schedule where the rate per day is even, resulting in linear production.

LINE BALANCING   Assigning and redesigning work done on an assembly line to make work cycle times at all stations approximately equal to produce a flow line.

LINEAR LAYOUT   Laying out various machines in one straight line. This type of layout makes it difficult to reallocate operations among workers.

MANUFACTURING LEAD TIME   *See* Cycle Time and Lead Time.

MANUFACTURING RESOURCE PLANNING (MRP II)   Material Requirements Planning evolved into the closed loop MRP system, which then evolved into Manufacturing Resource Planning. Technically, MRP II includes the financial planning as well as planning in units; it also includes a simulation capability. From a management point of view, MRP II means that the tools are being used for planning and scheduling all the resources of a manufacturing company.

MASTER PRODUCTION SCHEDULE (MPS)   For selected items, it is a statement of what the company expects to manufacture. It is the anticipated build schedule for those selected items assigned to the master scheduler. The master scheduler maintains the schedule and, in turn, it becomes a set of planning numbers that "drives" MRP. It represents what the company plans to produce expressed in specific configurations, quantities, and dates. The MPS should not be confused with a sales forecast, which represents a statement of demand. The master production schedule must take forecast plus other important considerations (backlog, availability of material, availability of capacity, management policy and goals, etc.) into account prior to determining the best manufacturing strategy.

MATERIAL REQUIREMENTS PLANNING (MRP)   Computers were used shortly after their introduction into manufacturing companies to explode material requirements or do "requirements generation." With the introduction of time phasing, these material requirements could be expressed in detail in specific time periods, usually weeks. By this time, netting out gross requirements against on-hand and in-process inventory had become a well-accepted technology. Modern MRP, therefore, is an approach for calculating material requirements not only to generate replenishment orders, but also to reschedule open orders, to meet changing requirements. Today, it is thought of more as a scheduling technique than an inventory ordering technique.

MIXED-MODEL PRODUCTION (OR SCHEDULING) Making several different parts or products in varying lot sizes so that a factory is making close to the same mix of products that will be sold that day. The mixed-model schedule governs the making and the delivery of component parts, including outside suppliers. The goal is to build every model, every day, according to demand.

OUTBOUND STOCKPOINT Designated locations near the point of production on a plant floor to which produced material is taken to await pickup by a pull system.

POINT OF USE Receive material to where it is needed.

POKAYOKE Designing the work process to eliminate human mistakes. Devices may be attached to machines to check automatically for abnormals in the process (called autonomous machines). The devices can automatically shut down the line if something is not as it should be.

POST-DEDUCT TRANSACTION *See* Backflush.

PROCESS CONTROL Controlling the production process by checking the quality while the work is being done.

PRODUCTION PLAN The agreed-upon strategy that comes from the production planning function.

PULL SYSTEM *See* Demand Pull.

PUSH SYSTEM Usually refers to how material is moved on the factory floor. Push indicates that material moves upon completion of an operation to the next operation. An alternative method is called demand pull.

QUALITY Conformance to requirements.

QUALITY CIRCLES An organization of five to twelve people who normally work as a unit for the purpose of seeking and overcoming problems concerning the quality of items produced, process capability, or process control.

QUEUE   A waiting line. In manufacturing, the jobs at a given work center waiting to be processed. As queues increase, so do average queue time and work-in-process inventory.

QUEUE TIME   The amount of time a job waits at a work center before setup or work is performed on the job. Queue time is one element of total manufacturing lead time. Increases in queue time result in direct increases to manufacturing lead time.

REPETITIVE MANUFACTURING   Production of discrete units, planned and executed via a schedule, usually at relatively high speeds and volumes. Material tends to move in a sequential flow.

ROBOTICS   Replacing functions previously done by humans with robots that can either be operated by man or run by computer. Hard-to-do, dangerous, or monotonous tasks are likely candidates for robots to perform.

ROUGH-CUT CAPACITY PLANNING   The process of converting the production plan and/or the master production schedule into capacity needs for key resources: manpower, machinery, warehouse space, vendors' capabilities, and, in some cases, money. Product-load profiles are often used to accomplish this. The purpose of rough-cut capacity planning is to evaluate the plan prior to attempting to implement it. A synonym is resource requirements planning.

ROUTING   A specification of the sequence of operations required to manufacture a product.

SAFETY STOCK   (1) In general, a quantity of stock planned to be in inventory to protect against fluctuations in demand and/or supply. (2) The average amount of stock on hand when a replenishment quantity is received. (3) In the context of master production scheduling, safety stock can refer to additional inventory and/or capacity planned as protection primarily against forecast errors and/or short-term changes in the backlog. This investment is often under the control of the master scheduler in terms of where it should be planned. Sometimes referred to as overplanning, market hedge, or buffer inventory.

SAFETY TIME   In an MRP system, material can be ordered to arrive ahead of the requirement date. The difference between the requirement date and the planned in-stock date is safety time.

SALES AND OPERATIONS PLANNING   The function of setting an overall level of manufacturing output (the sales and operations plan), expressed in families, to form a company game plan. Its prime purpose is to establish production rates that will achieve management's objectives of supporting the sales plan and customer service objectives, and of raising or lowering inventories and/or backlogs, while usually attempting to keep the production work force relatively stable.

SETUP The process of changing dies or other parts of a machine in order to produce a new part or product. Also called changeover.

SETUP TIME The time required for a specific machine, assembly line, or work center to convert from production of one specific item to another.

SINGLE MINUTE EXCHANGE OF DIE (SMED) A setup time of less than ten minutes, developed by Shigeo Shingo in 1970 at Toyota.

STOCKLESS PRODUCTION Synonym for Just-in-Time.

STOCKPOINT A designated location in an active area of operation into which material is placed and from which it is taken. It is not necessarily a stockroom isolated from activity. A way of organizing active material for easy flow-through production.

TOTAL QUALITY CONTROL A system built into all phases of a manufacturing organization, from design engineering to delivery, that attempts to ensure that no defective parts are produced. The basic elements include process control, easy-to-see quality, insistence on compliance, line stop, correcting one's own errors, 100 percent check, and project-by-project improvement.

TOYOTA PRODUCTION SYSTEM A compilation of many different manufacturing elements that deal with issues such as environment, quality, and setup reductions, as well as planning, scheduling, and execution techniques.

U-LINES Production lines shaped like the letter "U." The shape allows workers to easily perform several different tasks without much walk time. The number of work stations in a U-line is usually determined by line balancing. U-lines promote communication. *Also see* Cellular Manufacturing and Group Technology.

VENDOR SCHEDULER A person whose main job is working with vendors regarding what's needed and when. Vendor schedulers are in direct contact with both MRP and the vendors. They do the material planning for the items under their control, communicate the resultant schedules to their assigned vendors, do follow-up, resolve problems, and advise the master scheduler when purchased items will not arrive on time to support the schedule. The vendor schedulers are normally organized by commodity, as are the buyers. By using the vendor scheduler approach, the buyers are freed from day-to-day order placement and expediting, and therefore have the time to do cost reduction, negotiation, vendor selection, alternate sourcing, etc.

VENDOR SCHEDULING   A purchasing approach that provides vendors with schedules rather than individual hard-copy purchase orders. Normally a vendor scheduling system will include a business agreement (contract) for each vendor, a weekly (or more frequent) schedule for each vendor extending for some time into the future, and individuals called vendor schedulers. Also required is a formal priority planning system that works very well, because it is essential in this arrangement to routinely provide the vendor with valid due dates.

ZERO DEFECTS   Synonym for total quality control.

ZERO INVENTORIES   Synonym for Just-in-Time.

Bibliography

BOOKS

Crosby, Phillip B. *Quality Is Free.* New York: NAL, 1979.

Feigenbaum, A.V. *Total Quality Control.* New York: McGraw-Hill, 1961.

Ford, Henry. *My Life and Work.* Sydney, Australia: Cornstalk Publishing, 1927.

Hagen, John T. *A Management Role for Quality Control.* New York: American Management Association, 1968.

Hall, Robert W. *Zero Inventories.* Homewood, Ill.: Dow Jones-Irwin, 1983.

Juran, J.M. *Quality Planning and Analysis.* New York: McGraw-Hill, 1980.

Monden, Yasuhiro. *Toyota Production System.* Norcross, Ga.: Institute of Industrial Engineers, 1983.

Peters, Thomas J., and Waterman, Robert H., Jr. *In Search of Excellence.* New York: Harper & Row, 1982.

Schonberger, Richard J. *Japanese Manufacturing Techniques.* New York: Free Press, 1982.

Schorr, John E., and Wallace, Thomas F. *High Performance Purchasing.* Essex Junction, Vt.: Oliver Wight Limited Publications, 1986.

Shingo, Shigeo. *Study of the Toyota Production System.* Tokyo: Japan Management Association, 1981.

———. *A Revolution in Manufacturing: The SMED System.* Stamford, Ct., and Cambridge, Mass.: Productivity, Inc., 1983.

Wallace, Thomas F. *MRP II: Making It Happen.* Essex Junction, Vt.: Oliver Wight Limited Publications, 1985.

PERIODICALS

Bauer, Clarence C. "Black and Decker at Tarboro, North Carolina." *AMES Periodical News Source,* October 1985.

Brooks, Roger. "Teaming up for JIT." *Modern Materials Handling,* December 1985.

Garwood, R. Dave. "Kanban Myths." *P&IM Review and APICS News,* July 1984.

———. "The Americanization of JIT." *P&IM Review and APICS News,* September 1984.

———. "Explaining JIT, MRP II, Kanban." *P&IM Review and APICS News,* September 1984.

———. "Just-in-Time for Accounting." *P&IM Review and APICS News,* February 1986.

Goddard, Walter E. "Kanban Versus MRP II." *Modern Materials Handling,* November 1982.

———. "Under America's Kimono—Kokomo!" *Modern Materials Handling,* December 6, 1983.

———. "Messages." *Modern Materials Handling,* July 6, 1984.

———. "Shop Floor Control: Its Role in Manufacturing." *Modern Materials Handling,* September 7, 1984.

———. "Push Versus Pull." *Modern Materials Handling,* September 1984.

———. "Frustration Index." *Modern Materials Handling,* December 10, 1984.

———. "Kanban Versus MRP." *Modern Materials Handling,* February 1986.

———. "Dreamers and Doers." *Modern Materials Handling,* March 1986.

Goddard, Walter E., and Brooks, Roger B. "Just-in-Time: A Goal for MRP II." *APICS Conference Proceedings,* 1984.

Kaplan, Robert S. "Cost Accounting: A Revolution in the Making." *Corporate Accounting* III, no. 2, Spring 1985.

Landvater, Darryl. "Banana Peels." *Infosystems,* November 1984.

Sessions, Robert E. "Just-in-Time—A Revolution in Management." *General Electric Corporation,* November 1985.

Oliver Wight Survey. "Control of the Business." *1985 Newsletter.*

Oliver Wight Newsletter. ''Straight Talk on Just-in-Time,'' July 1985.

————. ''Self-Inflicted Labor Wounds,''July 1985.

————. ''Survey Reveals Benefits of MRP and MRP II,'' July 1985.

————. ''OK, We Have Higher Labor Costs. Now What?'' August 1985.

Winter, Drew. ''Just-in-Time Works.'' *Job Shop Technology,* December 1985.

Index

A

Adair, Charlene, 14, 32, 166
APCOM, 97, 152-3, 155-6

B

Backflushing, 71, 161
Bacon, Ray, 35, 40, 48-9, 57-9, 69-70,
    144, 166
Bar-coded label, 1-2
Baver, Clarence, 119
Bently Nevada, 35, 40, 59, 69-70, 144-
    5, 154
    Business planning, 96
    Employee recognition, 57-8
    Financial measurements, 166
    Marketing, 150-1
    Product design, 89, 125
    Schedule flexibility, 99
    The thinking worker, 48-9
    Vendor relations, 144
Bill of Doing It Right, 179-80
Bills of Material, 21, 122-4
Black and Decker, 13, 32, 43, 45, 50,
    54, 70, 83-5, 145, 154, 160, 163,
    175
    Bill of material, 123-4
    cellular manufacturing, 21, 117, 119-
    21
    Education, 34
    Employee communication, 30
    Vendors, 131-2, 136-7

Bletscher, Mark, 133
Buffer stock, 16
Burch, Rob, 14, 43, 45, 105

C

Capacity Requirements Planning, 104-6
Cellular manufacturing, 13, 19-21, 117,
    119-22
    Economic feasibility, 120-2
Central Commodity Management Group,
    137
CEO, 7
Chain of command, 26
Competitive edge, 6-8
Component costs, 23
Computerization, 21
Corporate Accounting, 166
Crosby, Phil, 15, 75-6
Cummins UK, 122
    Flexible workforce, 53
    Software, 160
Cycle time, 19

D

Davis, Duane, 59, 121, 128
Demand pull, 111-5
Deming, W. Edward, 76-8
Deming Prize, 76
Distribution Resource Planning, see DRP
Donigan, Kevin, 57-8, 114

DRP, 153-4
Drucker, Peter, 180
Dulle, Bill, 150

E

Early retirements, 59
Economic order quantity, 63
Edison, Thomas, 59
Education, 33-7
Electronic data interfaces, 163
Elimination of waste, 12
End-of-month crunch, 17
Environment, 25-8, 32, 43-5
    Communication, 29-31
    Education, 33-7
    Teamwork, 15, 38-42
Expediters, 17

F

Facilitator training, 51-2
Fact transfer, 33
Feigenbaum, A. V., 78
Financial Measurements, 165-7
FitzGibbon, Dave, 149-50
Flexible labor, 52-4
Flexible manufacturing, 13
Flip chart, 50
Flow industries, 162
Forbes Magazine, 57
Ford, Henry, 5-6
Foreign competition, 4
Frustration index, 173
Fuji Xerox, 83
    Product design, 89-90

G

Global competition, 4, 25
Global economy, 4
Global population, 4
Good, Ken, 45, 131-2, 175

Group facilitation, 39
Group technology, 20

H

Hall, Robert, W., 34
Hewlett-Packard, 1-4, 14, 31-3, 39-41,
    44, 50, 55, 72, 82-3, 86, 98
    Accounting, 166, 171
    Demand pull, 112-3
    Education, 34
    Employee evaluation, 58
    Freight consolidation, 143
    Rate generator, 104
    Software, 160
    SPC, 87-8
    Teams, 51
    Vendors, 131-2, 135-6
Hot lists, 17
H-P
    see Hewlett-Packard

I

In Search of Excellence, 31
IBM, 59-60
Ilsco, 149-50
Incentive, 55-6
Incoming inspection, 1
Industrial barrier, 5
Information flow, 3
Institute of Management Improvement,
    66
Inventory flow, 10-11

J

Japan, 7, 19, 66, 83
    Deming, W. Edward, 76-8
    Employee suggestions, 29-30
    Engineers, 40
    Flexible labor, 52
    Key to success, 4-5

Oil crunch, 11-12
Pooling requirements, 142
Product design, 89-90
Quality, 76-7
Quality circles, 85
Vendors, 133, 139
Japanese Manufacturing Techniques, 34
JFI, 167
Johnson, R. Michael, 51
Juran, J. M., 76

K

Kanban, 11, 107, 139, 141
Kanban-type signals, 112
Manual cards, 21
Kaplan, Robert S., 166-7, 169, 172
Kelley, Walt, 25

L

Landry, Pierre, 4, 42, 52, 75, 83, 128,
134-5, 153, 157, 171
Lauria, Joe, 40
Layoffs, 59
Lead times, 19, 21
Leaden Rule, 127
Line balancing, 13, 120
Line stops, 82

M

Machine setup time, 19
MAN, 113
Manufacturing offshore, 6
Marketing, 148-52, 155-7
Design engineering, 154
Distribution resource planning, 153-
4
Material flow, 13
Material shortages, 17
McGregor, Douglas, 58

Measurements, 19, 23, 168-71
Financial measurements, 165-7
Frustration index, 173
Operational measurements, 172-3
Mistakes, 59
Mixed model scheduling, 13, 99-102
Material As Needed
see MAN
Material Planning and Execution, 102-4
Mt. Fuji effect, 77

N

Nissan, 94, 141
Demand pull, 113
Electronic data interfaces, 163
Vendor deliveries, 139
Vendor scheduling, 162
NIT, 91
No-layoff policies, 59

O

Omark, 13-15, 33, 50, 58, 64, 79, 82-
3, 102-4
Accounting, 170
Demand pull, 112, 114
Employee involvement, 47-9, 57
Flexible labor, 53
Preventive maintenance, 91
Priority, 44-5
SPC, 88
Vendors, 131-3, 147
Opocensky, Jack, 89, 125
Ouchi, William, 38
Outbound queue, 111
Overhead absorptions, 23
Owen, Ann, 54

P

Paralysis through analysis, 31
Parrish, Ed, 154

Past-due purchase orders, 17
Pearson, Vern, 15, 44-5, 49, 79, 82, 170
People involvement, 14-15, 23
Pilot project, 32-3
Plant distribution, 1
Point-of-use inventory, 13
Pokayoke, 84
Preventive maintenance, 3, 12, 16, 90-1
Process-sensitive product design, 124-61
Procurement, 1
Product design, 89-90, 124-5
Profit sharing, 56

Q

QIC, 82
Quaker Oats, 168
Quality at the source, 16
Quality circles, 16, 39, 85-6
Quality Information Center
    see QIC

R

Rate generator, 104
Recognition, 57-8
Repetitive manufacturer, 3
Respect builders, 48
Retraining, 59
Rice, Don, 152-3, 155-6
Ringerwole, Harvey, 49
Routing files, 21

S

Safety stock, 10
Schedules, 17, 21, 93-6, 98, 103-5, 97,
    109-10
    Mixed model scheduling, 99-102
    Sales and operations planning, 97
    Short lead times, 108
    Small order quantities, 108
    Toyota Material Planning, 106-8

Toyota Production System, 106
    Valid, 18
Schonberger, Richard J., 34
Shingo, Shigeo, 19-20, 34, 66
Shull, Joe, 150-1, 154, 156
Setup times, 2
    reducing, 13, 19-20, 120
Single Minute Exchange of Die, see
    SMED
Skill modules, 53
SMED, 19, 45, 66-7
Software, 21, 159-60, 164
    Multiple inventary locations, 161
    Vendor scheduling, 162
    Electronic Data Exchange, 163
SPC, 16, 78, 87, 90
Stable Master Schedule, 98
Statistical Process Control, see SPC
Steelcase, 14, 23, 43, 49, 57, 105
    Cellular manufacturing, 121-2
    Demand pull, 112
    Environment, 40
    Motivation, 55
    Priority, 45
    Profit-sharing, 56
    Quality circles, 86
    Setups, 68, 71
    Shop floor control, 104
    Teams, 38, 41, 51
Stephans, John, 166
Stockroom computer terminal, 1
Study of the Toyota Production System,
    34
Supplier Quality Engineers, 87
SWAT teams, 50
System software, 19

T

Tachikawa, 94, 141
    Vendor scheduling, 162
Team meetings, 50-2
Teamwork, 38
Tektronix, 13, 98
    Checklist, 177-79

Inspection costs, 73
Lead times, 155
Product design, 124
Teams, 38-9, 51
Vendors, 138
Tennant Company, 30, 43, 58, 72, 83, 99-102
   Accounting, 171-2
   Cell assembly line, 120-1
   Demand pull, 112
   Employee recognition, 57
   Product design, 124-5
   SWAT teams, 50
   Vendors, 128, 133-4
   Worker visibility, 50
Testability, 125
The Harbor Study, 5
The Human Side of Enterprise, 58
Time barriers, 19
Top Management Communication Interface, 133
Total Quality Control
   see TQC
Toyota, 12
   Demand pull, 112
   Vendors, 139
Toyota Motor Company, 21
Toyota Motor Corporation, 11
Toyota Production System, 11, 17-18, 94, 106-9, 113, 139
TQC, 13, 16, 78-85
Two-bin system, 107, 112

U

U-lines, 121
Users, 37-8

V

Vendor flexibility, 31
Vendor performance, 18-19, 127-8, 134, 142-4, 147

Consolidating suppliers, 137
Education, 135-6
Electronic link, 138-41
Impact on accounting, 145-6
Quality, 86-8, 138
Vendor scheduling, 129, 131, 162
Vendor visibility, 31, 129-33
Vredenberg, Gary, 38

W

Warne, Jack, 79
Wight, Oliver, 4
   Reinforcement, 36
WIP, 1-2, 7, 10, 13, 16, 19, 72
Work-in-progress
   see WIP
Worker visibility, 49-50
World competitive standing, 4

X

Xerox, 4, 13, 18, 31, 51, 75, 137-8, 142-3, 145, 148, 157, 163-4
   Accounting, 171
   Benchmarking, 83
   Education programs, 34, 37
   Electronic network, 138-9, 146
   Flexible labor, 52
   Lead times, 153
   Product design, 89-90
   Quality circles, 86
   Transportation costs, 72
   Vendor education, 135-6
   Vendors, 42, 86-8, 127-9, 133-4, 147

Z

Zero Defects, 12-13, 75
Zero Inventories, 34
Zero time, 19